'I CAN FEEL THEM GETTING CLOSER.

IT HAS BEEN MONTHS SINCE MY SUBDUCTOR MAJORIS LAUGHED THAT BARKING LAUGH OF HERS IN MY FACE. I HAD MADE NO SENSE, I FREELY ADMIT. VAGUE PREMONITIONS WERE ALL I HAD: THE SOUND OF SLOW DRIPS, THE FEEL OF UNDULATING MOVEMENT, A GOLDEN LIGHT TOO DISTANT TO OFFER COMFORT. HOW DOES ONE COMMUNICATE A NAMELESS DREAD?

EMPEROR FORGIVE ME, BUT I AM SCARED.

EVEN NOW, AFTER SO MANY NIGHTS PUMPED FULL OF STIMMS, MY BODY BREAKING DOWN THROUGH LACK OF SLEEP, I FEEL IT DRAWING NEARER. MAYBE IF MY SECURITY DETAIL ALLOWED ME TO SLEEP, TO RECOVER, I COULD MAKE SENSE OF IT. BUT THEN I MIGHT DREAM. I CAN'T ENDURE ANOTHER DREAM LIKE THE LAST ONE.

"ONE MORE NIGHTMARE LEAKING OUT OF THE CICATRIX MALEDICTUM," THE SUBDUCTOR MAJORIS HAD SNEERED. I WONDER NOW WHY SHE HADN'T SEEN IT HERSELF. MAYBE SHE HAD AND WAS AFRAID. SHE SHOULD BE, WE ALL SHOULD BE. I HAVE FELT THE SCRATCHING IN MY HEAD, FELT THE CARESS OF SOMETHING SLICK IN MY MIND. TESTING. QUESTING.

THE SPREADING DARKNESS IS BEFORE ME NOW EVEN WITHOUT SLEEP. IT BUILDS INTO A THUNDERHEAD OF SHADOW. IT POOLS INTO OCEANS OF BLACK INK. I SEE THE CANDLES OF WORLDS ILLUMINATED BY THE MINDS OF MY BROTHERS AND SISTERS, FIRST DIMMED AND THEN EXTINGUISHED. IT'S CURIOUS, MANY OF THE FLAMES SWELL, THEIR LIGHT TOO BRIGHT, BEFORE THE SHADOW REACHES THEM.

LOCKED HERE IN MY WARDED AND SANCTIFIED QUARTERS AWAITING CENSURE, I CANNOT TELL WHETHER OR NOT WHAT I SEE IS SOME ECHO OF THE FUTURE, SOME PORTENT OF ABOMINABLE TERROR. I PRAY MY GAOLERS WILL TIRE OF MY EXISTENCE BEFORE LONG.'

- Personal journal of Keisha Ananguru, Subductor Astropathicus Minoris, Thyraen Relay Station.

BLOOD OF BAAL

CONTENTS

PRODUCED BY GAMES WORKSHOP IN NOTTINGHAM

With thanks to the Mournival and the Infinity Circuit for their additional playtesting services

Games Workshop Ltd, Willow Rd, Lenton, Nottingham, NG7 2WS

games-workshop.com

INTRODUCTION

The Cicatrix Maledictum yawns wide. Half of the Imperium of Mankind is cut off from the guiding light blazing from Terra. In the darkened Imperium Nihilus, the Blood Angels and their successor Chapters fight for their very survival against hordes of ravenous xenos, for the Tyranids will not be sated.

The region of space known as the Red Scar is an irradiated and crimson-lit swathe of star systems and gas nebulae. Through its bio-rich sub-sectors, a tendril of Hive Fleet Leviathan had wormed its way – uncountable living vessels, each filled with swarming horrors. The Tyranids had invaded the Cryptus shield worlds, their rapidly evolving monstrosities overwhelming the Imperial defences in just a few days of ferocious destruction. A single cry for aid escaped the suffocating Shadow in the Warp. It was received by the Blood Angels, whose home world of Baal lay directly in the line of the Tyranids' rapacious advance.

Chapter Master Dante's call to arms was answered by many of the Blood Angels' successor Chapters. As the Tyranids bore down upon the Baal System, their numbers blotted out

the stars, raining spores filled with xenos warriors upon the planet Baal and its moons. The death toll mounted on both sides, but the aliens' losses were rapidly replaced. On every front, the depleted Space Marines were pushed back. The sons of Sanguinius were on the brink of extinction when the Great Rift suddenly ripped wide and engulfed much of the Baal System in a storm of warp energy.

Through the devastation wrought upon the encircling hive ships, the Cicatrix Maledictum was, at first, Baal's saviour. Now, however, the insidious effects of the Great Rift's psychic trauma are felt throughout the Red Scar and present a new and terrible threat. A shadow grows, and the region's citizens begin to feel a horrible scratching in their skulls…

IN THIS BOOK

This book is part of Psychic Awakening, an ongoing series set in the aftermath of the Great Rift. It contains an overview from the perspective of the noble sons of Sanguinius – the Blood Angels and their successor Chapters – and the most voracious of xenos, the extragalactic Tyranids.

Inside you will find:

- The unfolding story of the battles in the Red Scar.
- A battlezone and mission to echo the narrative of Blood of Baal.
- Updated rules for the Blood Angels and Flesh Tearers, including datasheets, Relics, Stratagems and more.
- A host of rules content for the Tyranid hive fleets, including customisable adaptations.

A RED FEAST

When the Great Devourer turned its galaxy-spanning hunger to the Imperial star systems scattered throughout the Red Scar, the Blood Angels stood in their path. The sons of Sanguinius resisted the xenos tirelessly, fighting not only to safeguard Imperial space, but to defend their home world of Baal itself, for the Chapter's very survival was at stake.

By giving a name to the myriad Tyranid incursions, the Ordo Xenos believed they understood them. The hive fleet code-named Leviathan was recorded ravaging sectors to the galactic south, yet invasions by creatures exhibiting similar colourations and tendencies struck at isolated sectors all over the galaxy. In reality, Leviathan's tendrils attacked from beneath the galactic plane, unlike the other hive fleets known to Mankind. Regions could gain no advance warning of attack by monitoring this hive fleet's serpentine course. Questing shoals of hungering bio-ships appeared seemingly at random from the frozen emptiness beyond the galaxy. In this way, many bio-rich worlds of the Red Scar were scoured of life before the Imperium could muster any defence.

The Red Scar flares like an angry weal over the holo-charts of the Ordo Astra. Its thousands of stars all shine a shade of crimson, tinting the worlds and gas clouds of the region with the colour of spilt blood. Each system is cursed with ferocious radiation emitted by these scarlet suns, and life there is exceptionally hard. But the Imperium never shirks from harsh conditions when there are valuable resources to acquire. Though billions died to embed permanent settlements, hundreds of the Red Scar's systems eventually rang to the noise of human industry beneath the ruddy stars.

The tendril of Hive Fleet Leviathan that wound its way through and around the Red Scar was but a single proboscis of the gestalt organism that emerged from the intergalactic void. Nonetheless, it consisted of the greatest number of hive ships the Imperium had ever recorded. One curling spur of Leviathan's presence

in the Red Scar would later be termed the Cryptoid Tendril, for in its path were the shield worlds of Cryptus. This populous binary system was just one of countless territories threatened by the Tyranids, which the Imperium took decisive steps to defend.

Vital for its refined promethium and advanced solar energy arrays, Cryptus received reinforcement from several Astra Militarum regiments and other Imperial forces. Guardsmen, tanks and even a mission of Battle Sisters were sacrificed to defend Cryptus, but, one by one, the system's worlds were overcome. When Cryptus' signal reached Baal, the shield worlds' struggle was already known to Commander Dante, Chapter Master of the Blood Angels. Whether the system stood or fell, the Tyranids would inexorably advance upon the Chapter's home world of Baal, but, if the xenos could be made to bleed enough at Cryptus, then maybe Baal stood a chance.

The Blood Angels pushed back the xenos at Cryptus with furious assaults, but the unending waves of Tyranids pouring into each battlezone threatened to grind the sons of Sanguinius down. It was then that the war upon the shield worlds woke their ancient inhabitants, the Necrons, whose tomb had orbited the binary stars for aeons, unknown to the Imperium. It was only a wary pact made with these fleshless aliens that saw Cryptus' worlds

'We stood at Phodia for an age, but against such mindless hunger, we could never prevail. When I look upon the Angels of Baal, though, I see the hope I thought had been lost.'

- General Dhrost, Cadian 185th

finally flensed of Tyranids, though at great cost.

The surviving Blood Angels now made for Baal. Knowing the home world was at risk, Dante issued a summons to as many of the Blood Angels' successor Chapters as could be reached. Companies from almost every one of them answered the call. As the hive fleet drew nearer, the planet was fortified as it had not been for millennia. Even the able-bodied amongst its tribespeople were armed and stationed throughout the system, many within the fortress monastery upon Baal itself. Dante hoped it would be enough, for when the Tyranids of Hive Fleet Leviathan descended on Baal, their approaching bio-ships obscured the ruby stain of the Red Scar with their numbers.

The ravening swarms fell upon Baal like a deluge. A flood of teeth and chitin poured towards the firing Space Marines, as the air became a toxic soup of alien spores and caustic rain. One after another, the Blood Angels' carefully layered defences were overcome by weeks of savage fighting. Amidst the relentless tumult, the Tyranid invasion rapidly adapted its tactics, heedless of the thousands of beasts lost every moment. As defences fell to infiltrator-organisms, fresh swarms poured forth to meet the blazing guns of the Blood Angels. It was then that the galaxy itself screamed.

From the Eye of Terror to the Eastern Fringe, the Great Rift tore the galaxy asunder and Mankind's realm was divided. Warp storms ravaged many of the Imperium's traumatised survivors, and the Baal System was not spared, becoming caught in a roiling gale of energy. Clustered in orbit like predators around a dying animal, the Tyranid hive ships had been lashed mercilessly. When the Blood Angels were next able to focus their augurs heavenward, the xenos ships had vanished.

Upon Baal, continent-spanning swarms of monstrosities and scuttling weapon-beasts remained, reverting now to their more bestial instincts. The Blood Angels did not understand what had occurred in orbit, but sensed a chance to regain the initiative now that the Tyranid hordes on Baal were severed from the star-spanning intelligence directing them. The xenos did not fall back before the Blood Angels' counter-assaults, however, but instead flung themselves forward with greater hunger and ferocity.

The Blood Angels teetered on the brink of extinction. Though the hive ships were gone, the Baal System's worlds still teemed with xenos. It was but one system of thousands in War Zone Baal, which encompassed the Red Scar and its fringes. Within each one, the Tyranids swarmed and feasted.

WAR ZONE BAAL

Spanning the entire Red Scar and many systems on the region's fringes, War Zone Baal has suffered through the largest Hive Fleet Leviathan invasion the Imperium has ever recorded. The Blood Angels and their successor Chapters stand in the aliens' path.

Dante is pushing the Tyranids back from key installations, employing his vast military resources as Regent of the Imperium Nihilus with consummate skill. Each xenos tendril denied worlds to feast on, or diverted and cut off, is another step towards reclaiming the Red Scar. But the bio-fleets of Leviathan are vast, and worlds defended from their hunger are by no means reprieved.

THE WHITE
VAULT FALLS

Between deadly masses of interstellar rock, Huntsman Squadron's escort carriers and their Fury interceptors duel with cyclopean spore-casters.

THE OCCULU
STARS

GROLLAH
ASTEROID WELL

ADEPTUS ASTRONOMICA
STATION (SILENCED)

VITRIA SYSTEM
(REINFORCEMENT UNDER WAY)

MINDSHARD
BROODKIN

mind-voice of Governor Prendas'
ear-old son is heard by senior
opaths upon worlds around the
an Channel.

THE FALSE BEACON

ET LEVIATHAN

RYBAN CHANNEL

SATYS SYSTEM
(CONSUMED)

CORNYS
(AETHERIC DISRUPTION)

Galactic Plane

THE RED WILDERNESS

THE LIGHT OF MARTYRS

GAVENDOR

Three reave-brigades of the 51st Parthic Aerosans are despatched reinforce Gavendor amid reports insurrection among its indentees

GAMMA IV SYSTEM
More than twenty space stations and orbital platforms glitter around the worlds of the Gamma IV System. The system's astropathic relay, cut off entirely from the light of Holy Terra, reaches out to its sister stations for aid.

ASHALLON
In the Kranos System, the industrial planet of Ashallon becomes lost to the Imperium's sight. Astropaths see nothing there but a well of deepest black.

THE ANGEL'S HALO

BAAL SYSTEM
(BLOOD ANGELS
CHAPTER PLANET)

ADEPTUS ASTRA TELEPATHICA STATION
(NUNC DIMITTARY)

BHELIK ALPHUS
The fortress world of Bhelik Alphus weathers the surging warp storms and the waves of xenos assaults, relying on firmly built fortifications and its unfailing loyalty to the Imperium.

QUARANTINE ZONE
(ABANDONNED)

CRYPTUS SYSTEM
(INVESTIGATION PENDING, REF.
EMERGENT NECRON THREAT)

GRACINTH PONTUS SYSTEM
Gracinth Pontus fills with refugees fleeing the central Red Scar, before a tendril of Hive Fleet Leviathan rises from the galactic plane to attack the system. The xenos find its worlds full of biomass to devour.

TRADING STATION ROTARIS 309

ARCHANIS SHEAR
The scarlet web of dust clouds constituting the Archanis Shear faces two encroaching tendrils of Hive Fleet Leviathan. Its seven systems, once inextricably linked in a network of support, are all isolated by the insidious Shadow in the Warp.

DISUSED EMPYREAN GATE

THE OBSCURA VEIL

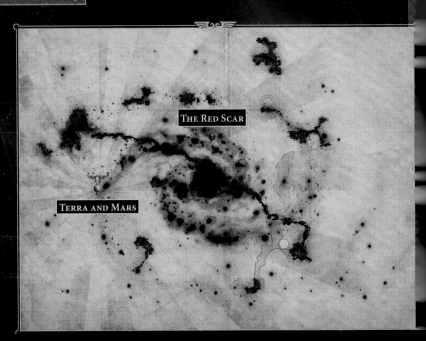

THE RED SCAR

TERRA AND MARS

DUTY'S DEMAND

The Blood Angels battling the Tyranids on Baal were faced with the possibility of utter destruction. Yet the opening of the Great Rift brought salvation unlooked for. As the Tyranids fought on with savage instincts, a figure from another time swept out of the tortured warp with reinforcements and dolorous tidings.

> *'Our light shall not gutter out beneath this shroud of blackness. These xenos filth will not prevail. I vow to you – all of you who share the Angel's noble blood – we will cast down these beasts, we will sunder their hosts, for their end has come!'*
>
> *- Commander Dante, Lord of the Angelic Host*

The Blood Angels and their successors fought for the world of Baal with sharpened blades and blazing bolt-fire. Where ammunition ran dry or combat knives were blunted, they lashed out with kicks and punches. Enhanced musculature and hardened ceramite were pitted against snapping maws and raking talons. At stake was the survival of the entire system. Baal's mortal citizens fought too, for they knew that no mercy could be expected from the Tyranids. All believed it could be Baal's final hour, and they fought with the fury of those with nothing left to lose.

Beyond the spore-choked skies, the Tyranid bio-ships in orbit had been brutally swept into oblivion by the warp storms that roiled in the wake of the Great Rift. In their place, the turbulent void miraculously disgorged a new fleet. Approaching Baal, the incoming ships transmitted Imperial identifiers to the Blood Angels – revealing that they hailed from Terra – but the chrono-idents were so corrupted that Baal's logisticians could ascertain no fixed origin time. These were ships of the Indomitus Crusade, the immense force which was spreading out from Terra to reclaim and defend Mankind's dominion. They found the Blood Angels' positions on Baal's surface to be steadily contracting before the encircling Tyranid swarms. The ships unloaded searing barrages of macro-cannon shells into the xenos to stall their advance, before releasing wings of attack craft and countless dropships. The warriors they carried were Primaris Space Marines who owed their genesis to the far-reaching tactical acumen of Roboute Guilliman, and it was none other than the Avenging Son himself who now coordinated the Imperial attack.

Clad in the colours of the Blood Angels, the Flesh Tearers and other Chapters of Sanguinius' line, the incoming waves of Adeptus Astartes warriors inspired the depleted defenders to resurgent acts of savagery. Many Imperial lives were lost as defenders and crusaders hammered the Tyranids away from their lines. However, after days of battle, the combined Imperial armies stilled the aliens' impetus across half of the planet, giving the Blood Angels breathing room to consolidate. Gathering for the first time since the battle for Baal had commenced, Dante and the other Chapter Masters formally accepted the Primaris reinforcements and the arcane technology required to create more. Only Gabriel Seth of the Flesh Tearers harboured reservations about the gift's implications, but his warriors had been impressed with those Primaris Space Marines who fought in their livery.

Guilliman shared with the Chapter Masters the terrible tidings of the Great Rift and its consequences for Humanity, even as many of these leaders stared at him, struck by the presence of one hailing from a time of legend. Guilliman concluded by appointing Commander Dante as Regent of Imperium Nihilus, a responsibility both deeply humbling in its honour and immeasurably weighty in its magnitude. With swarms remaining upon the home world and its sister planets, the future of Baal was by no means secure. Yet Guilliman's fleet made preparations to move on, for there were regions whose peril was far greater. The sons of Sanguinius now drew plans for a counter-offensive to cleanse the rest of the system.

Revitalised by reinforcements and fresh purpose, Dante and the commanders of the successor Chapters struck out from positions that had nearly been the site of their doom. Strike forces assembled by the surviving allies swept forward to rid Baal of the Tyranid hordes. The Blood Angels were determined to capitalise on the creatures' severed link to the Hive Mind, not knowing how quickly it could be re-knitted. Weeks of further bloodshed ensued, and Baal's already battle-torn deserts were churned to mud as they became soaked with blood and ichor. The Tyranid dead piled high to form a stinking, unending bloodscape.

The might of the Primaris Space Marines was proved beyond question in theses battles, and

the Blood Angels wasted no time in beginning to muster further waves of this new breed of warrior. Many of the young tribesmen who had bravely defended Baal were remade as Primaris Space Marines, having proved their worth ten times over during the horrific invasion. They were not the only ones to undergo transformation, for the Blood Angels' sinister Chief Librarian, Mephiston, undertook the dangerous crossing of the Rubicon Primaris.

Together, the Imperial armies finally crushed the last of the Tyranid swarms. However, not for a moment did the Blood Angels believe that Baal was entirely cleansed of the xenos presence; there were likely wounded or cut-off creatures still hiding in desert caves or buried beneath the dunes of sand and corpses. And who knew how long the countless spores which had rained down on the planet would remain dormant, before bearing their hideous fruit? The task of hunting down the xenos remnants fell to surviving tribesmen and neophyte Space Marines, but finding lone organisms paled against the immense duties now placed before Dante – duties which the relative lull in hostilities now allowed him to appreciate more fully.

The Blood Angels and their successors had been mauled. Despite the much needed influx of Primaris Space Marines, no Chapter on Baal stood at full number. Even those that were still strategically functional had lost immeasurable tactical strength, including

veterans of centuries, ancient and irreplaceable wargear, and even many Chapter Masters. Ranged against them were the predatory infestations on the other worlds of the Baal System, and many others spread throughout the Red Scar and its fringe regions. The fate of the Tyranid bio-vessels that had vanished from Baal's orbit remained unknown, but Dante was assured by his blood-weeping Astropaths that no similar disappearances had occurred elsewhere. Quite possibly the Tyranids had not even noticed the loss; their numbers were legion, their hunger limitless.

Lord Guilliman's reports of the galactic turmoil shocked Dante. Throughout the Imperium Nihilus, numberless terrified worlds were beset by horrors. Who knew how many systems Mankind's enemies had already leapt upon, sensing weakness? Wielding the authority of Terra, the Blood Angels were to be the Emperor's hand beyond the Great Rift. Dante resolved to make this a gauntlet dripping in the blood of Mankind's enemies.

The Lord of the Angelic Host gathered his senior advisors and fellow Chapter Masters. Together, they determined that reclaiming the remainder of the Baal System must be their first priority. With the home system secure, Dante would then set in motion the Angel's Halo – an ambitious plan of reconquest that would strike at three nearby systems to establish them as staging posts for further expansion.

To support these three chosen theatres, Dante and his fellow Chapter Masters despatched forces to fight holding actions and reclamation operations throughout the region, intercepting or delaying Tyranid reinforcements. Dante did not hesitate to call upon the full breadth of his newly conferred authority as Regent of the Imperium Nihilus. If the Red Scar was to survive, the Angel's Halo could not be allowed to fail.

THE SPREAD OF SHADOW

War Zone Baal reeled under the onslaught of the Tyranids, its thousands of systems writhing as they were consumed. Each prey world was isolated by the suffocating psychic voice of the Hive Mind, the psykers on those planets tortured to the point of insanity.

The Tyranids spread throughout the flourishing systems of the Red Scar, even to those weakly bound to its fringes. An invisible psychic miasma accompanied their advance; a phenomenon the Imperium had long ago learned to fear as the Shadow in the Warp. It engulfed entire systems, cutting off cries for help and crippling the defenders' ability to flee. As the Tyranids came to infest the entire region, there was nowhere they were not felt. Astropaths went insane trying to send the simplest of visions. When the Great Rift split reality in the midst of this terror, many psykers in the Red Scar dared to believe that the galaxy was responding to the Tyranids' unnatural psychic taint.

The Imperium fought back viciously against the Tyranids throughout the Red Scar's systems. The Blood Angels and their successor Chapters formed the blade's edge in these bloody actions, but the Space Marines were few. Many battlezones comprised only a small number of squads of Sanguinius' sons, supported by Astra Militarum, or forces from forge worlds or sacred shrines. The Blood Angels encountered panic and terror amongst the surviving populations. Desperate riots broke out, people screamed uncontrollably, and kin fought kin. Trepidation was understandable before the encroaching hordes, but in some cases the violence had to be ruthlessly stamped out.

In the Di'aden Sub-sector, the Librarians of the Angels Sanguine witnessed this terror spawned violence even amongst their allies. Screaming guardsmen dashed their heads against ferrocrete walls, and Skitarii warriors became caught in fevered logic loops, oily blood pouring from their emitters. When the Tyranids' smothering psychic pall fell over a world, even the Librarians' fortified minds strained to endure its touch.

The Imperium had long known that non-psykers felt the Tyranids' psychic presence as a shroud of unnatural dread, but never had its effects been witnessed to this degree. Stretched as thinly as they were across War Zone Baal, the

Blood Angels and their successors could ill afford such bewildering afflictions amongst the ranks of their allies.

While the exact source of these disturbing phenomena could not yet be fathomed, a further problem faced the war zone's populations. Since the opening of the Great Rift, the Black Ships that normally collected tithes of psykers from Imperial worlds had not been seen within the Red Scar. It was rumoured that these clandestine vessels employed select Navigator Houses and operated out of extensive facilities across the galaxy. If they could not reach the Red Scar to remove potential psykers, the consequences for the region might prove catastrophic.

More and more psykers appeared in the refugee camps to which so many civilians had been shipped like grox. Each psychic mind represented a threat to the Imperium's safety, and the Librarians of the Blood Angels and their successor Chapters saw their responsibility clearly. If the Black Ships could not discharge their duty, then the Space Marine psykers would have to act. Thus a great collective of Librarians took up watch over the refugee psykers, though it tore them away from their duties on the front lines. The Librarians tested the minds of as many of the aberrant humans as they could, probing for any psychic weaknesses.

It was well that the Librarians undertook this work, but its scale was monumental. The levels of psychic potential they found amongst the human refugees went beyond anything that could be explained by the absence of the Black Ships. The Librarians uncovered many fledgling psykers struggling to comprehend or control their new-found powers. Once identified, they were isolated and subjected to invasive psychic interrogation to determine the

manner of threat they posed. Yet, for every psyker so screened, many others lost control before they could be found. Some were horrified by the acts they committed, while others revelled in their unbridled power.

The Tyranids did not fail to notice this unexpected new weakness amongst their human prey. The Hive Mind observed through the senses of its almost limitless progeny, and responded as it always did. With unnatural speed, invasion swarms across the immense breadth of the Red Scar adapted. Soon, Blood Angels strike forces encountered broods of psyker-beasts on every battlefield. Veterans of past Tyranid wars had seen the aliens adapt in this way, but usually only in response to the pure psychic might of Adeptus Astartes warrior-mystics. Now, xenos strains wreathed in coronas of crackling bio-sorcery were reported upon battlefields where there were no Librarians at all. To the Blood Angels on the front lines, it seemed clear that the xenos had sensed the absence of Space Marine psykers and sought to take advantage by harnessing their own psychic might.

Upon some worlds, the Imperium was able to counter-strike with sufficient power to prevail against the ravenous Tyranids. Yet such victories were few, for often the Hive Mind's concentrated use of psyker-beasts crushed the sanity of Mankind's defenders. Under such creatures' baleful gaze, entire squads of guardsmen writhed in psychic torment before dropping as one. Even the sons of Sanguinius fell, their armour cracked open by lances of psychic witchfire.

Every battlefield of War Zone Baal, it seemed, was saturated with the power, the terror, and the unpredictability of the warp.

Post-statis Addendum — z./+bI1. <<Ex Tenebris Dal>>

As the report makes clear, my lady, our efforts to secure new specimens from the Red Scar systems have suffered greatly. Even my contacts among the xenos traffickers and dealers in bio-esoterica have been strangely unable to furnish me with viable samples – despite persuasion. Their usual avenues of procurement have evaporated. It is as if the xenos of the Red Scar are actively avoiding even the most tangential contact with Humanity. Our puritan fellows would rejoice, no doubt, but as a hunter, I need to know what has suddenly marked us out for avoidance by my quarry.

I have served the Holy Ordo for more than a century, yet never have I felt more isolated. Never have I felt the immense distance of the interstellar void more acutely. Where once the gaze of my augmetics beheld multitudinous prey, my febrile imagination now casts us as the exposed and vulnerable morsel.

*Rhova Targ,
Reclamator Alpha, Ordo Xenos*

++Transmission Origin: Purgatus++

STARS RED WITH BLOOD

The Blood Angels' home world was saved, but the cost had been terrible and the war was far from over. Faced with the enormity of the Tyranid fleets and the numberless bio-horrors they carried, the Blood Angels and their successor Chapters fought on nobly, launching the Angel's Halo offensive to take the fight to the stars.

Not all of the Blood Angels' successor Chapters that had survived the Battle for Baal continued to fight in the region. Many Chapter Masters took their newly inducted Primaris Space Marines and left, while some planned to return to and fortify their own holdings. Others redeployed at Dante's request to strategically important systems outside the Red Scar, preparing the way for the liberation of the wider Imperium Nihilus. Those Chapters that remained pledged to continue aiding Dante and the Blood Angels. Some, such as the Flesh Tearers, fought in the name of their shared lineage. Others did so in deference to Dante's title of Regent of Imperium Nihilus, for their commanders had witnessed Roboute Guilliman bestow that honour upon the Bringer of Sanguinius' Light.

The redeployment and reinforcement of the Blood Angels and their successors was no swift task. While new battle-brothers were trained, wounds healed and repairs made, small forces braved the churning warp to reconnoitre the very nearest systems.

His Chapter returned to fighting strength, Dante coordinated the retaking of the Baal System himself, taking a squadron of ships to the outer world of Kheru; a scrub-covered moon of a gas giant, used by the Blood Angels as a monitoring station. The Tyranids had originally been drawn to the planetoid by the immense reserves of complex gases locked in its crust. Their hive ships were now gone, dispersed by the fury of the warp storms, but hordes of weapon-beasts still befouled the moon's small sensoria-cities. If Dante could reclaim this infested part of his Chapter's home system, it would form a strong centre from which the Angel's Halo could expand. The Blood Angels launched their initial landings and the battle began in earnest.

While Dante fought to secure dominance of the Baal System, Gabriel Seth took the Flesh Tearers out into the void. The Angel's Halo strategy called for the taking of three initial targets, which Dante had termed the Points of Grace, to be seized as the Imperium's forces spread outwards in an expanding wave from the Baal System. These points were strategic foci that were vital to the wider purging of the Red Scar, by virtue of their position or their assets. Each of the three Points of Grace could be reached by a series of very short warp jumps plotted around scattered astropathic relays and sub-stations. Yet, even attempting these caused loss of life and severe damage to the largest of ships.

Seth volunteered the Flesh Tearers to take the first Point of Grace – the planet Ashallon in the Kranos System. This industrial world was a key supplier to many systems, but Dante had chosen it for another reason. Navigators and Astropaths from the Blood Angels fleet had reported that the system was completely lost to their arcane sight. Many systems in the Red Scar were shadowed, but the darkness surrounding Ashallon was denser than most. More disturbingly, this shadow was growing; something lurked there, spreading its influence. Few in the Imperial armies could agree on what it might be, but Seth knew in his heart that it could not be allowed to continue.

Meanwhile, the Blood Angels and Angels Encarmine sent Vanguard forces to the second Point of Grace – the linked space stations and orbital platforms of the Gamma IV System. These facilities contained a significant astropathic relay which made the otherwise uninhabited system a regular way station for ships undertaking perilously long journeys. No word had

THE DEMOCRACY OF DEATH

With the arcane bio-technology to create Primaris Space Marines and genetic samples of unprecedented purity revealed by Archmagos Cawl, hopes were kindled. Perhaps the growing curse of the Black Rage could finally be arrested. Within the breasts of the Sanguinary Priests, desperate belief clutched at the assurances made by the Tech-Priest. The genetic lineage would be undiluted. The scions of Sanguinius would be cleansed.

There were doubters and naysayers. Some posited that the closer to the Angel's purity the genetic samples were, the closer to his sacrifice their warriors would be, thus intensifying the death visions brought on during the eve of battle. Others questioned the wisdom of eliminating the curse at all, claiming that surely in willing themselves to overcome and suppress the madness, they maintained the strength and nobility of their primogenitor.

The battle-brothers newly inducted into the Blood Angels and their successors in the aftermath of Baal's salvation proved to be worthy of their Chapters. Whether survivors of the original warriors brought to Baal by Guilliman's fleet or matured using Cawl's imparted technology, they were strong and pure of heart. But hope in these times can be treacherous.

It was the Angels Encarmine who first revealed to Commander Dante the induction of Primaris Space Marines into their Death Company. Since then, the Blood Angels and each of their successor Chapters have seen their Death Companies filled just as readily with wearers of ebon-painted Mk X power armour. While some commanders lamented that their Primaris battle-brothers would not now herald a new beginning, all Chapter Masters recognised what it truly meant; that the Primaris Space Marines were true inheritors of Sanguinius' legacy.

---

been received from the bonded armsmen employed by the Adeptus Astronomica to protect the site, and the Vanguard warriors were tasked with ensuring its security or learning of its fate.

Having vowed to reclaim the planet identified as the third Point of Grace, Captain Sendini of the Blood Angels 5th Company assaulted the fortress world of Bhelik Alphus. Granted reserves from the 9th Company and a significant number of the Armoury's remaining assets, Sendini did not believe in being over-cautious. The firepower at his command would, he believed, allow the Blood Angels to destroy whatever Tyranids had managed to make it past Bhelik Alphus' formidable defences. Once secure, the planet would provide the sons of Sanguinius with a strong anchor-point from which assaults on other systems could be launched.

Unbeknownst to the Blood Angels and their allies, the Leviathan fleets swarming through the Red Scar were more than aware of events in the Baal System. Synaptic imperatives passed from one

organism to another, between fleets that were many light years apart. Leviathan's experience in many parts of the galaxy had given it the opportunity to learn. It was familiar with Mankind's varied armies, with the way in which they moved through the void and defended prey worlds. Through an aggregated stimulus and response on a vast scale, the hive fleet ensured that its organisms surrounding the Baal System went into overdrive: adapting, modifying and devouring.

Dante also dispatched smaller missions in support of the Angel's Halo strategy. Ships carrying no more than a few squads undertook short warp jumps to relieve embattled convoys of materiel

or refugees. They tested Tyranid forces for weakness, and conducted lightning-fast vertical insertions to perform assassinations and extractions. All the while, the ships' augurs strove to increase Dante's knowledge of both the Tyranids' disposition and the state of the warp storms across the Red Scar. The fragmentary reports these forces were able to send made for grim reading.

The surging warp storms born in the aftermath of the Great Rift showed no signs of calming. The Shadow in the Warp was in evidence throughout the entire Red Scar. Tyranid hive fleets carved through many Imperial systems, and wherever their malignant touch reached, madness flowered. The approach of the Tyranids' hive ships appeared to coincide with claims of horrific psychic phenomena.

Hope was in short supply, but not yet extinguished. Dante's attacks from Baal had prepared the way for further forays, and with the increasing numbers of Primaris Space Marines being created, there was still a chance they could prevail.

EXECUTION'S EDGE

The Blood Angels tore towards the last major infestation of the Baal System, determined to eradicate the Tyranids. Yet the aliens' loss of their hive ships had dulled neither their instincts nor their fangs.

Sec chanl Angelis.
<Astr. Senioris
Haq, cr. Scarlet
Blade>>

I cannot bear it any longer, the pain is too intense! It is all around me. A multitude of dissonant voices. Human voices! Inane, wordless babbling – there is no form to them, they are not abiding by the approved praxis for this or any other sector.

My kind? Whoever they are, captain, they are not 'my kind'. I have travelled the Sixteen Sectors ever since I gave my eyes to His Imperial Majesty. I am fluent in the astropathic forms of these and a dozen more. I can disentangle the gutter thoughts of 'my kind' who have spent too many years with Rogue Traders, but these are the brays of mindless children. They are undirected, the mix of emotions too overwhelming to focus on. I do not know who they all are.

Wait, you're … coming to the astropathic choir chamber? There is no need, we … I cannot. No, I quite understand my position, captain.

Yes, my lord, we will keep trying to reach Bhelik Alphus.

++END TRANSMISSION++

Blood Angels Vanguard forces spearheaded the assault against the Tyranids on the semi-desert world of Kheru. From orbit, it was apparent that the xenos were clustered around the fortifications erected by Kheru's dwindling Blood Angels garrison. The entire Imperial presence on the arid sentinel world was bottled up in four fortified sensoria-cities in the southern hemisphere. The Tyranids had surrounded these sites and were assaulting them in waves. Though cut off from the influence of the Hive Mind, the swarms were far from directionless as Dante had hoped; it was clear that some kind of control was still exerted over them.

Lieutenant Perdaelus led the force that advanced upon Sensorem Primus, the largest of the planet's facilities and its capital. When the Tyranids had invaded Kheru, its human garrison had succumbed as quickly to madness as to the aliens' bio-weapons. However, the Blood Angels posted to the planet when Baal was fortified had defended it with dogged determination, holding their positions for several months. With the Tyranids pouring their main strength towards Baal itself, the sensoria-cities on Kheru had been able to marshal their reserves of ammunition, but these were on the verge of running out when Dante's ships arrived.

Perdaelus and his Reiver Squads made a vertical insertion via grav-chutes, deploying two miles from Sensorem Primus. Arriving towards sunset, the blood red light of the Baal System's star masked their descent. Covert squads of Infiltrators and Incursors who had

worked their way from separate landing zones now made contact. Out of the deepening shadows stalked also the Chief Librarian of the Blood Angels, Mephiston. Perdaelus had not been briefed as to the Lord of Death's presence, and he welcomed the sinister battle-psyker warily.

The Infiltrators and Incursors had amassed a wealth of information concerning the tactical situation at Sensorem Primus. The sensoria-city stood at the foot of a cliff which shielded its delicate arrays from rogue vox-gheists emitted from the south, but meant its defenders could not withdraw in that direction. Waves of Tyranids attacked the city's barricades, broods of weapon-beasts fighting with claws or firing acidic gobbets that screeched through the air. In their midst stalked larger bioforms – leader-beasts that bore diamond-hard talons and weapon symbiotes that spat living projectiles. All the while, the city's automated guns and remaining Blood Angels defenders fought to keep the beasts at bay.

The Vanguard struck as Baal's star sank to the horizon. Arcing smoke grenades landed amongst the Tyranids, and the air filled with sounds of cracking chitin and erupting alien ichor. The Infiltrators and Incursors advanced from cover to cover along an ancient riverbed, firing ceaselessly. Attacking several broods at once, the Blood Angels spread out from their initial line of advance, each squad working in synchrony with their battle-brothers.

The Tyranids reacted instantly, turning to face the greater threat at their rear. Hormagaunts bounded over their dead through the dense fog of smoke and reeking fyceline. Bolt shells, unimpeded by the thick haze, consistently found their mark, but where one xenos fell, three more clawed their way forward. The swarm was now at the Blood Angels' throats, talons instinctively aiming at armour joints and eye lenses.

The Reivers had waited for the optimum moment to strike. As one, silhouettes that had seemed part of the scrub became a blur of motion. Shock grenades exploded, and the Reivers' amplified roars sounded like predatory snarls of rage as their combat knives became blooded. Through the shifting smoke shrouding the swarm, Mephiston darted with uncanny speed, his hazy form outlined by arterial sprays. Death-screeches filled the air around him as flashes of psychic power lit up the smoke.

Then, the Vanguard suddenly withdrew. Reivers pulled back under the ferocious covering fire of Incursors, and Mephiston threw up shimmering barriers that defied the living ammunition of the foe. Upon the dusty riverbed's high banks, Eliminators previously motionless in pools of shadow now chose their moment to fire their silent bolt sniper rifles at high value targets amongst the Tyranids.

The xenos poured after the Vanguard in an animalistic surge. But Dante had been right to sense a lingering control over the xenos. While the main swarm instinctively pursued the Blood Angels, imperatives had pulsed outwards from the leader-beasts, and Lictors and Genestealers now sprang from the thin scrub at the Space Marines' flanks and rear. Lightning-fast claws and talons tore through Mk X armour, hewing a gory path through the Blood Angels' ranks.

Many assassin-beasts were taken out by pinpoint bolt-fire and sweeps of heavy blades, but the fighting was desperate. As night fell, a foul rain of spores began to descend from the sky as the leader-beasts' psychic impulses drove their forces to surround the Vanguard.

It was then that Dante's own forces entered combat. Tongues of flame speared from the night sky, illuminating red and golden warriors. As intended, Mephiston and the Vanguard had drawn the Tyranids away from the sensoria-city, stretching the aliens' reach and forcing them to fight on two fronts. Acting on the Vanguard force's information, the descending angels of Dante's Sanguinary Guard and Suppressors first targeted the leader-beasts, cutting the head from the serpent in flurries of heavy fire and blows of crackling encarmine blades. Mephiston and Perdaelus led the Vanguard to hammer the remaining broods and, after much bloodshed, the last traces of the swarm were finally put down.

A DARK PRESENCE

As Dante attacked the swarms in the Baal System, the Flesh Tearers plunged into the tortuous warp without hesitation to reach the key industrial world of Ashallon. A creeping psychic darkness was spreading from the planet. Uncaring of its cause or implications, the Flesh Tearers aimed to find and rend apart the blight's source.

Ashallon was hidden from the arcane senses of the Flesh Tearers' Astropaths and Navigators, their warp-sight blind to its condition. Some reported a notion that a hideous, slick mass of psychic accretion had built up around the system, while others were gripped by violent seizures as they tried to focus their warp-sight upon it. The Navigators could only take the fleet to the system's outer edge, describing visions of sliding down a stinking, black gullet. Approaching Ashallon, Librarian Jarrod pinpointed the source of the growing aura, a city-sized refinery in the planet's northern polar region. It was reachable only by a single megalithic bridge, the Via Celestos, spanning a toxic hell half a mile below.

The Flesh Tearers' ships passed Ashallon's orbital platforms, hanging shattered and dark above the planet. The massive structures bore gaping rents where Tyranid ships had forced their feeder tendrils in to gorge on the crews. Then, the Flesh Tearers themselves encountered Tyranids, bio-vessels still clustered in orbit, seeding the planet below with alien spores. Lance volleys blazed from the Imperial vessels, rupturing metres-thick cartilage, while bio-plasma and pyro-acid shot back at them. The violence of Seth's attack enabled dropships to descend through Ashallon's atmosphere. Within their holds, the mood was grim. Many battle-brothers had succumbed to the Black Rage, and every Flesh Tearer felt a simmering anger that threatened to boil into violence.

Ashallon's polar regions were subject to intense disruptive energies capable of tearing strike craft from the skies. This forced Seth to land armoured assets further south, denying him the direct orbital insertion that would have allowed his warriors to vent their rage quickly. Battle tanks and transports rumbled from the

ASHALLON

Ashallon's industrial heritage stretched back millennia, its city-sized refineries and crenellated furnaces dating from the time of the Great Crusade. These were interspersed with less ancient hive cities, built upon the deep foundations of former factorums. Each stood atop a warren of abandoned conduits and flues, gantry nests and echoing reservoirs, all slowly ground down by the hive city above them like a moraine beneath a glacier.

Though no records exist, it was held by some among the sector's noble families that Ashallon was once a forge world of the Adeptus Mechanicus; one of such magnificence that its rulers imperiously annexed system after system around it. This embroidered story told that the Council of Terra itself grew suspicious or jealous of Ashallon's rise and took the world forcibly, destroying its forge temples and executing its Tech-Priests. Variations on the tale postulated that the Council acted with the compliance of the Adeptus Mechanicus, whose own political machinations are opaque, or that somehow agents of Terra were able to remove knowledge of the world entirely from the Tech-Priests' records.

Such courtly gossip filled the days of those bored with power and filtered down the social scale, so that sump-grubbers and criminal gangs came to pass the story around like a fairy tale; one given credence by the occasional piece of archeotech dug up in the hives' bowels.

The clearest expression of Ashallon's magnificent past was the Via Celestos. This immense structure – more a statement of power than a bridge – linked the world's capital refinery city to the equatorial vat farms miles further south. A miracle of forgotten engineering, its buttresses soared skyward for half a mile above the befouled industrial landscape. Not merely supporting a single thoroughfare, the Via Celestos comprised an interweaving morass of transit ways; bisecting, curling, threading through each other. From orbit, it appeared that the capital reached out with a mass of questing tendrils.

drop point and reached the Via Celestos; the bridge soared so high over the polluted land that sickly mists obscured its foundations. Within the transports, squads of Flesh Tearers barely contained their rising ire, watched over closely by Chaplains. Still no broods poured out of the city, and the Chapter Master felt he was being drawn in. His suspicion proved prophetic when the skies darkened above the refinery ahead.

The dark cloud swiftly resolved into dozens of winged creatures which swooped down upon the Flesh Tearers. Spilling from their transports, the ebon warriors of the Death Company charged whatever they could reach, while Intercessors formed a firebase. Corrosive bio-ammunition, melting armour seals and burrowing into flesh, but the Flesh Tearers' firepower held the winged terrors at bay.

As the rushing waves of aerial attacks continued, Seth's forces picked up auspex warnings of foes closing from behind, the signals becoming stronger, larger. Horrors resembling mythic drakes plunged from the skies, spitting accelerated crystalline clusters that tore through armour plate. Turrets swivelled. Tracks span. As the Flesh Tearers column responded to threats from all sides, the escalating anger proved too much for some battle-brothers. With screams of rage, Intercessors broke ranks in ones and twos, racing towards whatever they now perceived the Tyranids to be. Out of the mists below, yet more xenos rose, spiralling around the gothic buttresses of the bridge.

Stalled, disintegrating, the Flesh Tearers were being dissected. As if to confirm their fate, a new cloud of dark shapes appeared in the east. Yet, from its midst came rockets and blinding beams of energy that swatted screeching Tyranids from the air. Valkyrie and Vendetta gunships had arrived. Only as they sped overhead could vox be

established. The remnants of the system's Aeronautica Imperialis had survived out of sight in Ashallon's darkened orbital platforms. Detecting the Flesh Tearers' strike force, they had fought through Tyranid swarms of their own to reach the Space Marines' position. The surviving Flesh Tearers snatched the opportunity created by the Imperial air assault to break out of the trap and surge onwards to the refinery city. Librarian Jarrod led Seth and his blood-hungry warriors to the source of the sickening psychic miasma – the city's half-ruined astropathic tower. There they would end it.

Under a gaping rent in the tower's roof, the Flesh Tearers found a bloated bioform in the remains of a spore sac. Veins of energy linked it to the twitching husks of slack-jawed Astropaths. It was some

breed of psyker-beast, Seth guessed, engorged with power like nothing he had seen. With a shout, Jarrod cleaved the nearest Astropath in two, before a screeched command filled the air. Monstrous xenos suddenly broke straight through the walls and tore the Librarian apart with crushing claws. Seth felt he understood – this thing was using the Astropaths, draining them to project its black will into the void. His chainsword Blood Reaver ripped through the air, shearing immense talons in half, each backswing messily beheading an Astropath. The Flesh Tearers unleashed their rage, driving their weapons again and again into the xenos with grisly fervour. The ruined tower was awash with gore when Seth finally plunged his churning blade through the psyker-beast's brain, freeing the system from its growing taint.

PREDATOR AND PREY

The fortress world of Bhelik Alphus was the shield of its sub-sector. Its garrison had held out bravely behind the planet's strong defences, yet the troops' resolve was faltering in the face of unexplained phenomena. Unknown to them, Blood Angels reinforcements neared, but other eyes were not so blind to the Adeptus Astartes' approach.

The Blood Angels strike force arrived at Bhelik Alphus in perfect coordination. The ships had been delayed and scattered by their winding path through the unquiet warp, but the final translation was flawless, and they re-entered realspace with a storm of firepower. Blasted with macro cannons, some bio-ships withdrew into the void, trailing frozen gouts of ichor, while others aggressively attacked. Even as the orbital battle raged, Blood Angels under Captain Sendini of the 5th Company made planetfall.

As the Blood Angels gunships descended, some squadrons peeled off. These carried task forces of Phobos-armoured Vanguard Space Marines, entrusted with obtaining caches of weaponry and technology. Bhelik Alphus was rumoured to harbour huge stockpiles of the flesh-melting mutagenic acid used to produce hellfire shells. Securing this substance for Dante's other forces would greatly improve their chances against the Tyranids elsewhere in the Red Scar.

The Blood Angels' primary target was the fortified port complex at Rhikan. Its besieged gatehouse was holding out, but the overrun city around it gave the swarms all the cover they needed. Xenos forays had so far been repulsed, but there

was no way for the Astra Militarum garrison to break out and shatter the horde with massed firepower. In accordance with strict strategic doctrines, the garrison had sent all of the port's soldiers to defend the gatehouse, but Sendini had no appetite for blinkered siege theory; he would secure Rhikan on his own terms. Within moments, the fluid adaptability of the Adeptus Astartes had identified the means to crush the swarm.

The Blood Angels gunships landed at the deserted port itself as Sendini gave instructions to the garrison commander to evacuate the fortress and join the Space Marines. It was

ruthless, but Sendini knew the advantage outweighed the cost; the Tyranids would be led where he wanted them. The commander's reply was almost lost in the noise of anti-air cannons sweeping the port's skies, but garbled words could be heard, describing horrifying incidents concerning his men. Of more strategic concern to Sendini were reports of severe seismic disturbances felt across Bhelik Alphus for months. Though the port itself had been stable of late, data inloads from the garrison's cogitators revealed that three outposts and their defenders had disappeared into suddenly yawning chasms.

On Sendini's instruction, the garrison abandoned the bunker complex that formed Rhikan's gatehouse. No longer held back by its defence guns, the Tyranids smashed into it. A trio of Carnifexes charged, their spined and plated limbs tearing through the reinforced portal, heedless of any damage to themselves. In their wake, hundreds of smaller beasts screeched and hissed as they chased the garrison making for the port.

Behind the gatehouse complex lay a loading area criss-crossed with servohauler tracks, and beyond that the port itself. Rhikan Port had been built within a natural depression, and tiers of control towers and basilicanums encircled its landing zones like an amphitheatre. As the garrison withdrew, Suppressors fired into the oncoming Tyranids, shadowing the Imperial soldiers until they reached the cover of the port buildings. Now, Sendini made his move.

From every fortified barbican, every shielded balcony, the Fire Support Squads of the strike force let fly. The deafening sound reverberated around the depression, from overlapping explosions to shrieks of propellant. Rhikan Port was turned into a killing field as the heavy weapons of Sendini's

own 5th Company and the 9th Company reserves shredded dozens of xenos every second. The first wave of Tyranids disappeared in detonations of gore and flame, but more were coming. At their officers' command, the garrison soldiers turned their firepower upon the xenos also. Volleys of irregular lasgun fire from the terrified men and women stabbed out, but their discipline was failing.

Suddenly, a rumble like an earthquake shook Rhikan, unheard over the din of weapons but certainly felt. The soldiers of the garrison staggered. Chunks of ferrocrete rained down, striking human, alien and Astartes alike, and fissures snaked across the port. This soon proved to be no natural earthquake.

Fountains of rock and earth erupted across the landing zone, many even bursting up within buildings. From them crawled sinuous hook-limbed monsters. In the centre of the landing zone the ferrocrete apron collapsed, revealing the ravaged foundations that lay beneath. A honeycomb of tunnel openings was exposed, and from every one crawled more and more Tyranids. Looking down, Sendini saw that the xenos had bored through solid ferrocrete. This was no quick accomplishment; the entire area had been well prepared.

Bulbous, floating creatures now advanced amongst the Tyranids still sweeping forward from the gatehouse. Their fluted spines crackled with power, discharging bolts of energy that incinerated soldiers and melted through power armour. A hulking leader-beast also waded through the lesser bioforms, its deliberate movements displaying a dark intellect. At the psyker-

beasts' arrival, a strange malaise seemed to take hold of the garrison. Soldiers screamed and clutched their heads. Some tore at their eyes or suddenly attacked their squad mates. Worse was yet to come.

The Blood Angels on the ground were forced to engage in individual squad combat, their cohesion and firepower reduced by the need to defend against the xenos now in their midst. They pulled back to second lines of defence as serpentine horrors slithered towards them at unnatural speeds. On upper balconies their battle-brothers slaughtered Tyranids still, but suddenly grasping claws and talons tore at their backs as broods of Genestealers burst from within the buildings.

Captain Sendini, fighting with his warriors in ever shrinking pockets, called in aerial support. When it arrived, it was only a fraction of what he had prepared. From orbit, the breathless shipmaster revealed that they were fighting for their lives, many of Sendini's gunships already defending against boarding actions. The bio-ships that had initially fled had returned with more of their kind – living vessels that must have hidden themselves motionless in the dark reaches of the system. Sendini mastered his frustration, his strategic acumen spurred into action even as he savaged the xenos before him.

It was then that the garrison's troops erupted with aetheric power. Soldiers vomited black flame or ejected ribbons of energy from flailing arms, consuming their fellow soldiers and xenos alike. The psyker-beasts and looming leader bioform advanced on them as more horrific phenomena manifested. Clearly these were the doings of the Tyranid witch-breeds, but whether any of the Blood Angels would survive to report this new horror, Sendini did not know. His warriors were dying, Bhelik Alphus was falling, and hope was fading fast.

Echoes of Awakening

The Cicatrix Maledictum stretches the length of the galaxy, and warp storms covering whole sectors ravage once-stable regions. From their depths pours the very stuff of the warp, fuelling manifestations of psychic power both miraculous and terrifying. Myriad reports reach the Imperial authorities, from the seemingly mundane to the crazed and unintelligible. All speak of some momentous event gathering pace.

+++

```
Multi-frequency vox transmission
in crypt-octarhic masking. Baal
Prime S.polar orbit.

This is the ion-trawler Red Dawn,
contracted to Explorator-Archis
Vherran. Request for immediate aid!

They're killing each other! The
followers of the Machine God are mur-
[transmission fragmented]-my men, the
servitors, dropship crew. Madness!

Magos Vherran is… was investigating
the octational xenos remains upon Baal
Prime. Our Astropath is dead, screams-
[uplink breaks]- We have received only
broken vox from the surface since,
binharic threats of exsanguination
protocols, but layered with distorting
vox-gheists. My vox officer swears they
are roars. It cannot be the Magos…

This is the ion-trawl-[data breakdown]
```

+++

Prepare, Gavendor! Your wait is almost over — the Day of Days is near! The star-angels' messages can be heard even by the faithless. Accept them and rejoice!

Graffiti on Gavendor Arbites precinct bastion. Penal indentees diverted to eradicate offenders.

+++

```
[Communicatus Prioritis —
Transgressio Ultima]
Security Protocol 6.3.11vx
```

'Inquisitor, I have collated the requested reports and these are addended. The Orks of the Rachen Nebula, until recently on the verge of collapse, appear to have been absorbed into the migrating forces of the one known as Bakrash. Their combined momentum parallels that of the tribes emerging from the Kebban Sub-sector. I urgently recommend the deployment of the entire Bhorean Aegis watch fortress. The unusual uniformity of the Orks' movements will be irrelevant once they no longer exist.

H.'

+++

```
Servo-recording recovered from
Facility Alphis orb. Gamma IV
```

My Lord Dante, I commit grave news to this servo skull in the hope that it reaches you. I can no longer guarantee delivering it in person. The moripatris sees more and more brothers lost to us. So far, we have been able to sweep the facility's lower chambers, searching for the substance while defending the perimeter against the Tyranids. Eliminator Sergeant Daenello had been chanting the rites after our Chaplain fell to the curse, but Daenello himself is now with the Death Company. Every day their number swells, more than I have ever seen. I do not know what will happen when we can no longer send them to meet the xenos.

```
++ My Lord, we found no survivors aboard
this facility. Our brothers inside had
been ripped apart, though security
protocols were still in place. My report
on the other facilities at Gamma IV
follows. ++
```

+++

```
Interrogation of Gregan Chorle,
Astropath Tharsis Class — awaiting
excoriation. Day 27.
```

I was disturbed more than I can say by the message. The psychic tidings my kind receive often carry many subtle layers — the original dispatch forms a kernel, and around that are woven imprints from each Astropath through whom it has passed. You will not understand, but for us, each of these layers adds shades of meaning, allowing us to trace the course a message has travelled. What I received from the southern Ultima Segmentum was wrapped in confusion. I peeled the layers back one by one, becoming more and more fearful. At their centre was… nothing. Like opening a sarcophagus and finding the black and rotten remains of life. An empty and blank message. From what? For whom? I cannot express how horrifying it was.

+++

The King! The King on his Throne! I've seen him stir, I've heard him speak. Cold and gold and old and bold, sing for your suppers you priests who scold!

Inv. Am221-8v 'flayed crew, trad.
station Rotaris 309'

I saw her at The Four Bells, reflected
in my glass of amasec. I say 'her',
but that may just be an old man's
fancy. No one there, though. Just those
stick-thin merchants whistling that
damn tune. Sickly pallor, void-born
no doubt. Barkeep reckoned they'd been
there a week.

The tune had really stuck with people,
he said. He was right — by the time I
left, everyone was humming it, trying
to think up words for it. You couldn't
go anywhere without hearing it. Didn't
seem to stick with me, though, can't
think why. Here, you ever find my two
deck officers? Never got back on board,
lazy scum.

Evidence 34t-12281: interview with
Void Captain Erafisk of the bulk
hauler Platos.

+++

Experiment Phi-ton-Beta

'Magos, the wards are failing. Are you receiving my
data transmission? I cannot assess what is happening.
The servitors have ceased operation and are not
responding. I do not know if they have suffered
massive overl… Attend, they are operational again.

They are not accepting noospheric imperatives. This is
intolerable. We may have to relocate the artefact.

They are moving now, praise the Omnissiah – no,
go the other way! – their lenses… No, back! Magos,
request immediate reassignment. Magos Theraton,
please respond. MAGOS!'

++Experiment abandoned. Assets
unrecoverable.

Conclusion: More data required.
Experiment Phi-ton-II/y to
be expanded.++

+++

[Vox-thief recording 8b\4-dvii —
factorum identee monitoring]

*'I picked up another echo of the message today. You know
the one, same as the others, the same 'invitation'. I've
ignored them before, but what if it's real? What if there
really is a place with people like me, who hear things? And
you, with your… What if this Crimson Mentor really can
free us and teach us? I can't hide forever, Josep. I won't.'*

Subject and interlocutor detained by local forces,
awaiting arrival of Black Ship *Yelantis*.

MISSIONS

'The swarm of dark motes crowds my vision, growing denser with each passing moment. Even the minds of my brothers and sisters grows dim, their beautiful light smothered.'

- Kendar Vulgis,
Astropath of the Spire Ebonar

BATTLES IN BLOOD

The rules presented on the following pages allow you to play games set in locations inspired by those found in the narrative of this book, as well as play through one of the most daring moments from the early stages of the Blood Angels' fight to rid the Red Scar of the Tyranid invaders. Will you fight alongside the elite scions of Sanguinius to cleanse the Baal System of xenos predation, or will you consume all prey before you to further the unknowable aims of the Hive Mind?

INTRODUCTION

This section starts by providing a new Theatre of War, shown opposite, that is designed to represent any one of the numerous battlefields across the systems within the Red Scar. Blasted by the harsh radiation of the stars found within this astronomical phenomena, fighting within these environs is both dangerous and prone to great risk, but their crucial location ensures conflict is rarely far away.

These rules can, however, be used to represent any location where the surface of a world has been decimated by radiation, be it originating from solar entities or as a direct result of the deployment of horrifically destructive weaponry.

On pages 26-27, a new historical battle is presented for use in narrative play. Delaying Action lets players fight through the heroic holding action led by Chief Librarian Mephiston to distract the Tyranid threat, thereby preventing the xenos horde from overrunning a beleaguered Blood Angels force. The mission describes how to lay out the battlefield in order to best reflect this specific battlefront, and provides new rules and Stratagems for use in this scenario.

THEATRES OF WAR

Just as the Psychic Awakening floods the Red Scar region, the Tyranids worm their way through its worlds. The organisms of Hive Fleet Leviathan are so numerous that no world is safe. The Blood Angels and their successor Chapters are forced to engage the ever-hungry xenos in a multitude of locations.

In this section you will find an exciting new Theatre of War to use in your games of Warhammer 40,000. Theatres of War offer new tactical challenges to enrich your games, and introduce new rules to represent many varied battle environments. Some modify the core rules, for example by altering the range of weapons. Some provide new rules for phenomena like dust storms, volcanic eruptions and earthquakes. Some grant additional abilities and Stratagems to certain units.

These rules are designed to reflect the desolate and irradiated planet surfaces of worlds within the Red Scar, but they are entirely optional and, so long as you and your opponent agree, they can be used in any Warhammer 40,000 game, set anywhere.

Agree which, if any, Theatre of War rules will be used when you are setting up the battlefield, before deployment.

THEATRE OF WAR: IRRADIATED WASTELAND

The worlds of the Red Scar have felt the malignant touch of their scarlet-hued stars for aeons. Fierce waves of debilitating radiation seep through the air and into the very ground beneath warring armies, sapping strength and blighting flesh. Some systems, like Baal itself, continue to suffer the pernicious effects of ancient weapons unleashed in a darker age, but whose horrific effects have lasted millennia.

Tough Going: Subtract 1 from Advance rolls made for **INFANTRY** units.

Weakness of Flesh: When resolving an attack made against an **INFANTRY** unit that is not wholly on or in a terrain feature, add 1 to the wound roll.

Burning Skies: Before deployment, roll off. Starting with the winner, each player places one Irradiated Dust Cloud marker on the battlefield. Irradiated Dust Cloud markers cannot be placed within players' deployment zones, or within 12" of another Irradiated Dust Cloud marker.

When resolving an attack made with a ranged weapon against a unit that is within 3" of any Irradiated Dust Cloud markers, an unmodified wound roll of 6 inflicts 1 mortal wound on the target in addition to any other damage.

Harsh Exposure: Subtract 1 from the Leadership characteristic of models in **INFANTRY** units whilst their unit is not wholly on or in a terrain feature.

ECHOES OF WAR
DELAYING ACTION

On Kheru, the Blood Angels' Vanguard forces and Chief Librarian Mephiston sought to draw the Tyranids of Hive Fleet Leviathan out, exposing the leader-beasts that held the horde together. High in the skies, Commander Dante awaited the perfect moment to descend with his warriors on wings of fire.

THE ARMIES

Each player must first muster an army from their collection. The Defender commands two detachments of Blood Angels. One detachment is a force of Phobos-armoured Marines commanded by Chief Librarian Mephiston, and the other an elite detachment of jump pack equipped Blood Angels led by Commander Dante. Neither Blood Angels detachment should include any models with the Flyer Battlefield Role, and the Blood Angels player should aim to split their force as equally as possible between these two detachments.

The Attacker commands the innumerable hordes of the Tyranids and should have approximately one and a half times the size of army as their opponent. If the players' armies are Battle-forged, they will also be able to use the appropriate Stratagems included with this mission (see opposite).

THE BATTLEFIELD

The Defender creates the battlefield. The battlefield should feature a mix of trees and light cover elements. An objective marker should be placed, as shown on the map here, to mark the location of the astropathic beacon that Mephiston and his troops are trying to activate, in order to guide Dante and his reinforcements down into battle.

DEPLOYMENT

After terrain has been set up, the Defender sets up the detachment that is led by Mephiston wholly within their deployment zone, with their remaining models placed in Reserve (pg 194, *Warhammer 40,000 Rulebook*). The Attacker then sets up their units wholly within their deployment zone. All units that are set up on the battlefield before the start of the first battle round must be set up wholly in their deployment zone.

FIRST TURN

The Defender has the first turn.

HERE THEY COME

Tyranids units arriving from Reserve must be set up wholly within 6" of the Attacker's Battlefield Edge, and more than 6" from any enemy models.

ANGELS OF DEATH

Blood Angels units cannot arrive from Reserve until the start of the fourth battle round, unless, when that unit would be set up on the battlefield, a friendly INFANTRY model is within 1" of the astropathic beacon marker.

BATTLE LENGTH

Use the Random Battle Length rules (pg 194, *Warhammer 40,000 Rulebook*) to determine how long the battle lasts.

VICTORY CONDITIONS

At the end of the battle, for each player, add up the Power Ratings of all the units that player still has on the battlefield, and whichever player has the highest total wins a major victory.

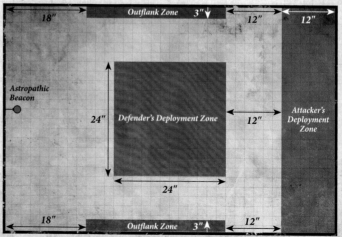

STRATAGEMS

In this mission, the players can use Command Points (CPs) to use the following bonus Stratagems:

DELVING TENDRILS
1CP

Attacker Stratagem
Once a hive fleet has sunk its talons into a prey world, there is nowhere its organisms cannot reach.

Use this Stratagem at the start of your Movement phase. Select one unit from your army that was set up in Reserve. That unit can be set up anywhere on the battlefield that is wholly within an Outflank Zone, and can move normally this turn.

HOLD THEM BACK
1CP

Defender Stratagem
Determined fire discipline allows Blood Angels to bleed the fury from the most devastating charges.

Use this Stratagem in your opponent's Charge phase. Select one unit from your army. Until the end of that phase, when resolving an Overwatch attack made by a model in that unit, a hit roll of 5 or 6 scores a hit.

WARP SHADOWS
2CP

Attacker Stratagem
The pervasive presence of the Hive Mind disrupts its enemies' coordination and communication.

Use this Stratagem when your opponent attempts to set up a unit on the battlefield from Reserve. That unit cannot be set up on the battlefield this turn. This Stratagem cannot be used after the third battle round.

DIRECT ASSAULT
1CP

Defender Stratagem
Blood Angels excel at pinpoint orbital assaults.

Use this Stratagem at the end of your Movement phase, before you set up a unit on the battlefield using the Jump Pack Assault ability. You can set up that unit anywhere on the battlefield that is more than 5" away from any enemy models, instead of more than 9" away.

DRIVEN IMPERATIVE
1CP

Attacker Stratagem
With a pulse of psychic command, the Hive Mind pushes its warriors minds and bodies to their limits.

Use this Stratagem in your Movement phase. Select one unit from your army. Until the end of the turn, when that unit Advances, instead of making an Advance roll add 6" to the Move characteristics of models in that unit until the end of the Movement phase.

VALIANT STAND
1CP

Defender Stratagem
Beyond their enhanced physiology, every Blood Angel is a warrior whose will to prevail against Humanity's monstrous enemies is embedded in their blood.

Use this Stratagem in any phase, when a unit from your army is targeted by an attack. Until the end of that phase, when a model in that unit would lose a wound, roll one D6; on a 6 that wound is not lost.

BLOOD ANGELS

'The penumbral cloud
these Tyranids clutch about
themselves holds no fear for
the Angels of Death. We will
rupture their suffocating shroud
and we shall bleed this host of
horrors dry.'

- Chief Librarian Mephiston

INHERITORS OF RAGE

In this section you will find new and revised content for the Blood Angels and their successors, including background, army-wide abilities, weapon updates, datasheets, psychic powers, Warlord Traits and Battle-forged army rules, as well as up-to-date points values and a name generator for the sons of Sanguinius.

This section is a supplement to *Codex: Blood Angels* – you will need a copy of that book to use the rules in this section.

Updated Abilities and Weapons

On pages 34-35 you will find new abilities and a number of weapon profiles for your Blood Angels army that replace those found in the codex.

Datasheets

The datasheets presented on pages 35-49 are new datasheets available for the forces of the Blood Angels. Where the same datasheets are found in both books, the datasheets found in this publication supersede any that exist in the codex. Note that, just as with the datasheets in the codex, when you include a **BLOOD ANGELS** unit from this section in your army that is not a named character, you can choose for it to be drawn from a Blood Angels successor Chapter. If you do, replace all instances of the **BLOOD ANGELS** keyword on that unit's datasheet with a successor Chapter keyword of your choice.

Vanguard Warlord Traits

Page 53 presents Warlord Traits that can be given to **BLOOD ANGELS PHOBOS** Warlords instead of the Warlord Traits found in the *Warhammer 40,000 Rulebook* or *Codex: Blood Angels*.

Stratagems

If your army is Battle-forged and includes any **BLOOD ANGELS** Detachments, the Stratagems on pages 54-56 can be used in addition to those presented in the codex.

Psychic Powers

Page 57 presents the Obscuration discipline, psychic powers known to **PHOBOS PSYKER** models.

Litanies of Battle

All **BLOOD ANGELS CHAPLAINS** know litanies and can generate them from the Litanies of Battle presented on page 58.

Relics of Baal

Page 59 presents additional relics that can be given to **BLOOD ANGELS CHARACTER** models from your army instead of those found in *Codex: Blood Angels*.

Special-issue Wargear

Page 60 presents relics that can be given to **CHARACTER** models from your army from Blood Angels Successor Chapters.

Flesh Tearers

Pages 62-63 presents the rules for fielding an army formed from the Flesh Tearers Chapter, a Blood Angels successor Chapter.

Name Generator

Page 64 provides a useful tool to help you forge a name for mighty warriors of your Blood Angels, further building the background and personality of your army.

Points Values

Page 65 presents updated points values for the Blood Angels to use in games of matched play or games that use a points limit.

'I fought to reach here from Cadia, through surging warp storms that threatened to tear us apart. I was too late to aid in Baal's salvation. But for my brothers lost defending our world, I swear by Sanguinius himself that these base creatures will die in the Red Scar!'

- Captain Sendini, Keeper of the Arsenal.

CHIEF LIBRARIAN MEPHISTON

A figure of awe and reverence amongst many Blood Angels, Mephiston carries the will and power of one who has overcome what no other Blood Angel has. Mephiston has battled through near-death to surmount the Black Rage, the curse that has afflicted the Blood Angels and their successors for millennia.

Mephiston was once Brother Calistarius, a promising member of the Blood Angels' Librarius, before he suffered the depredations of the Black Rage. The Curse of Sanguinius spares no rank or position, defying whatever gift of foresight those of the Angel's line have inherited. Calistarius was fighting before the walls of Hades Hive during the Second War for Armageddon when the Black Rage fell upon him, and he was duly inducted into the Death Company. He and others were fighting in the final assault of the Ecclesorium and, when the building collapsed, Calistarius was buried beneath tons of rock.

For days, the Librarian lay trapped. Tormented by visions brought on by the Black Rage, he teetered between life and death, sanity and eternal madness. Yet Calistarius did not succumb. Turning his gaze inward, the psyker confronted the Black Rage that burned within his very soul. Through sheer force of will he rejected it and cast it out. On the seventh night, he finally burst free from his entombment, reborn as Mephiston, Lord of Death.

Within his ravaged body, his gene-seed had awoken and wrought miraculous changes. He moved with a speed none could match, while his strength could pulverise the most resilient of flesh. In showers of blood he rent apart his enemies, as roving bands of Orks found to their cost. He returned to his Chapter, covered in the gory viscera of his foes, and forever changed.

Mephiston rose through the Librarius' ranks and now holds the vaunted office of Chief Librarian. He is held by most Blood Angels as an icon of hope, the first step on the road to the Chapter's salvation. If one has overcome the Black Rage, they say, then so can others. But there are some who wonder at the cost exacted from their brother. Taciturn and thoughtful, where once Calistarius was voluble and gregarious, some of Mephiston's battle-brothers are wary of what they see as a soul carrying a sinister burden.

With the means to develop Primaris Marines now in the Blood Angels' hands, Mephiston stepped onto the next path of his fate. Crossing the Rubicon Primaris, the Chief Librarian demonstrated the Chapter's embrace of their new battle-brothers in the most selfless way possible. What will come of this further transformation can only be guessed at. It is yet the latest line Mephiston has crossed, and the Blood Angels can only hope that this transformation will ease the Chief Librarian's burden, and not ultimately release the darkness that remains in Mephiston's soul.

HOST OF ANGELS

The battle-brothers of the Blood Angels are scions of the winged Primarch, Sanguinius, and host to the virtues and the flaws of their Primogenitor. They are staunch defenders of Mankind, with an instinctive gift for aerial combat, yet fight a constant battle against a dark inheritance.

The Blood Angels Chapter of Space Marines hails from the planet Baal. Since the rending opening of the Cicatrix Maledictum, their home world has lain in the Imperium Nihilus – cut off from the light of the Astronomican. While much of Mankind wails and cowers in this new era of terror, the Blood Angels stand firm before the many enemies who seek to hasten Humanity's demise. The sons of Sanguinius continue to bear their faith in the Imperium, just as their gene-sire did millennia ago.

CHAPLAINS

Chaplains are terrifying orators who inspire with bloody carnage as equally as with fiery sermons. They are the custodians of the Chapter's beliefs and enforcers of its discipline wherever necessary. Chaplains conduct the litanies that bind the battle-brothers together. Not only through solemn intonations within vaulted chambers, but also through shouted catechisms of hate, bellowed over the din of battle as their blunt weapons of office crush bones. They are incarnations of the Angels of Death, their black armour bedecked with leering skulls.

Blood Angels Chaplains fulfil another role, unique to the Chapters of Sanguinius' heritage. To them falls the responsibility of watching the Marines under their care for signs of the flaw. The Chapter and their successors harbour a genetic curse, one which manifests in visions of bloodshed. This is the Black Rage. Chaplains lead their battle-brothers in soul-calming masses, keeping a vigil for any Blood Angel who may be overcome. With the High Chaplain, Astorath the Grim, lies the duty of carrying out the final redemption of those whose souls cannot be saved. For others suffering the touch of the Black Rage, a chance to serve the Chapter awaits them in the Death Company.

DEATH COMPANY

On the eve of battle, when pulses quicken, some Blood Angels cannot suppress the images of betrayal and murder that stain their waking sight. In a fugue state, the afflicted are drawn back through the millennia to the dark days of the Horus Heresy, reliving the desperate fight on Terra and enduring the agonies of the Angel himself. They are led away by their Chaplains and inducted for the forthcoming battle into the Death Company. Armour is ritually re-painted black, with crimson saltires representing Sanguinius' wounds. Seeking death in battle, they are honoured by their Chapter with this final fight.

The Black Rage can afflict any Space Marine in whose veins runs the legacy of Sanguinius. It respects neither station nor the glorious deeds of those it corrupts. The brief hope that the Primaris Marines could somehow avoid its maddening touch has been contemptuously extinguished. Intercessors so burdened, whatever their original squad designation, are gathered together in sepulchral units. Upon the battlefield, their fervour lends them resilience beyond that of their peers, shrugging off what should be killing wounds. In whatever xenos or mutant they fight, the Intercessors see only the heretics of a bygone time. Already considered dead by their own Chapter, the delusion driven fury of the Death Company has slaughtered reeling foes on countless worlds. The Primaris Marines have truly been embraced by their Chapter – blood, body and soul.

SANGUINARY PRIESTS

Guarding the future of the Chapter as much as the Chaplains are the members of the Sanguinary Priesthood. This dedicated brotherhood carries out the arcane surgery required to create Space Marines and ensures the collection of gene-seed from the battlefield. Perhaps their greatest task, however, is maintaining the Chapter's genetic purity and seeking a cure for the flaw.

ARMOURED MIGHT

The anti-grav repulsor technology developed, or perhaps uncovered, by Archmagos Cawl has been central to many designs. The Repulsor Executioner sacrifices some of the transport capacity of its namesake for the increased capacitors and power cells required for its prodigious amounts of heavy ordnance. Capable of serving equally as a mainline battle tank or as secure transport for a Blood Angels squad, its silhouette, ploughing loudly over battlefield debris, has become a common sight. It is as welcomed by Baal's warriors as it is feared by their enemies. The Impulsor, meanwhile, is more lightly armoured, but its speed and ease of access has made it a natural fit for many Vanguard missions. Ferrying Primaris Marines in safety, its highly adaptable hard points mount an array of weaponry, and can be upgraded with more specialist wargear.

BLOOD ANGELS VANGUARD

The warriors of the Blood Angels' Vanguard squads are experienced forward operatives, skilled in covert missions and shock assaults. They often undertake assignments far from support, sowing disruption in enemy territory for extended periods before rising up from concealment to cause maximum carnage.

Primaris Marines of the 10th Company fight as Vanguard squads. Each specialises in aspects of reconnaissance, infiltration and the elimination of threats – from the disruption sown by Infiltrators and Reivers, to the aggression of the Incursors, and the clinical devastation wrought by units of Suppressors and Eliminators. Wearing a sub-pattern of Mk X Phobos armour, every warrior is trained for each role in turn. Primaris Space Marines keep these skills honed after progressing to other companies, and are able to don Phobos armour and reprise such duties when required.

Infiltrators lie in wait for days before moving swiftly into action. They are sabotage and disruption specialists, using omni-scramblers to confuse enemy signals. Often the first the foe sees of them are plumes of dense smog when they are already too close. Explosive shells from bolt carbines unerringly find weak points, fuel lines or eye lenses. Many squads include a Helix Adept, a medicae specialist trained by the Sanguinary Priests, who is able to keep the squad at peak efficiency in the field.

Though Incursors often deploy in concealed positions as well, their role is more direct. Under the cover of smoke grenades, they penetrate their foes' lines before unleashing death from occulus bolt carbines, or sundering installations and vehicles with a haywire mine. Neurally linked with multi-spectrum arrays, none escape their sights. Information culled from every source feeds directly into their visors, giving a preternatural tactical overview of the battle, and allowing them to predict every move of their doomed prey.

Reivers embody the terror of the Adeptus Astartes as no other. They drop via grav-chute like silent angels or emerge with rictus grins over the rims of previously secure parapets. Switching in the blink of an eye from secrecy to violent fury, they are shock troops without peer. Staggering foes, stunned by shock grenades, are shredded by armour-piercing bolts, or cut down by heavy-bladed combat knives. Slick with the blood of their victims, they almost appear to revel in the dark savagery that lies at the heart of every Blood Angel.

Each Invictor Tactical Warsuit is a stripped back Redemptor Dreadnought chassis. Its pilot is not the mortally wounded hero that rests within the usual sarcophagus, but a living member of the Vanguard. The pilot controls the immense construct with a selflessness of spirit that speaks to the true nobility of the Blood Angels. With its servos and reactor able to run almost silently, the Invictor is able to advance undetected alongside its Vanguard brethren. From here, the pilot lends tactical support with a variety of heavy weapons.

Seemingly from nowhere, the shots from Eliminator Squads can cripple an enemy's command structure in moments. These snipers can remain almost unseen, cowled in camo cloaks and deep in enemy territory, while keeping up a steady tally of kills from their high-powered bolt sniper rifles, or shattering heavy armour with las fusils. Some Blood Angels see little honour in the deployment of Eliminators, preferring to boldly fight the enemy face to face. Still, in these desperate times, all Blood Angels commanders recognise that every weapon must be brought to bear if Humanity is to survive.

Suppressors wear a heavy form of Mk X plate. As members of the Vanguard, however, they are not lumbering infantry, but bound in graceful leaps using powerful jump packs. Some squads descend from low altitude, their mass compensated for by grav-chutes. Held unwavering before them are the long barrels of accelerator autocannons, while the loop of ammunition feed coils behind. These devastating weapons punch out a stream of huge armour-piercing shells that are enough to drive back any who are not slain by the fusillade.

MK X PHOBOS

Of the sub-patterns of Mk X power armour, the Phobos designation has seen the widest array of adaptations. Invictor pilots illustrate the extreme versatility of Phobos armour. Suppressors, meanwhile, wear a fusion of elements common to both the Phobos and Gravis patterns.

Like all Primaris battle-brothers, officers of the Chapter fight in Phobos pattern armour whenever the tactical situation merits it. Captains and Lieutenants of all companies will lead missions into the enemy's heart wearing such plate, commanding equally silent warriors with undetectable battle cant. Librarians replace their Tacticus pattern raiment with Phobos armour when utilising the most subtle and illusory of their psychic powers, cradled in misdirection.

ABILITIES

All **Blood Angels** units in *Codex: Blood Angels* (excluding **Servitors**) gain the Angels of Death ability:

Angels of Death

The Adeptus Astartes are amongst the finest warriors in the Imperium.

This unit has the following abilities: And They Shall Know No Fear, Bolter Discipline, Shock Assault and Combat Doctrines.

And They Shall Know No Fear

The Space Marines of the Adeptus Astartes stand unafraid before the greatest terrors of the galaxy.

When a Morale test is taken for this unit, you can re-roll the dice.

Designer's Note: *With the addition of the Angels of Death ability, some units in* Codex: Blood Angels *will gain the And They Shall Know No Fear ability twice. Such units gain no additional benefit from this.*

Bolter Discipline

To a Space Marine, the boltgun is far more than a weapon – it is an instrument of Mankind's divinity, the bringer of death to his foes.

Instead of following the normal rules for Rapid Fire weapons, models in this unit firing Rapid Fire bolt weapons make double the number of attacks if any of the following apply:

• The firing model's target is within half the weapon's maximum range.

• The firing model is **Infantry** and every model in its unit remained stationary in your previous Movement phase.

• The firing model is a **Terminator**, **Biker**, **Centurion** or **Dreadnought**.

BOLT WEAPONS

A bolt weapon is any weapon whose profile includes the word 'bolt' (boltgun, bolt rifle, storm bolter, combi-bolter, hurricane bolter, etc.), and any Relic that replaces a bolt weapon. Rules that apply to bolt weapons also apply to the boltgun profile of combi-weapons, and the boltgun profile of Relics that replace combi-weapons.

For the purposes of this ability, a Rapid Fire bolt weapon is any bolt weapon with the Rapid Fire type.

Shock Assault

The Adeptus Astartes are elite shock troops who strike with the fury of a thunderbolt.

If this unit makes a charge move, is charged or performs a Heroic Intervention, add 1 to the Attacks characteristic of models in this unit until the end of the turn.

Combat Doctrines

When the Adeptus Astartes fight alongside their battle-brothers they employ a strict set of combat doctrines.

Models in this unit gain a bonus depending on which combat doctrine is active for your army (see below). If you have a Battle-forged army, units only benefit from this bonus if every unit from your army has this ability (excluding **Servitor** and **Unaligned** units). This bonus is not cumulative with any other rules that improve the Armour Penetration characteristic of a weapon.

At the start of the battle, the Devastator Doctrine is active. A combat doctrine remains active for the duration of the battle, though you can change which combat doctrine is active once at the start of each battle round after the first, as follows:

• If the Devastator Doctrine was active during the previous battle round, you can change it so that the Tactical Doctrine is now active.

• If the Tactical Doctrine was active during the previous battle round, you can change it so that the Assault Doctrine is now active.

Devastator Doctrine

The Armour Penetration characteristic of Heavy and Grenade weapons this model is equipped with is improved by 1 whilst this combat doctrine is active. For example, AP 0 becomes AP -1.

Tactical Doctrine

The Armour Penetration characteristic of Rapid Fire and Assault weapons this model is equipped with is improved by 1 whilst this combat doctrine is active. For example, AP 0 becomes AP -1.

Assault Doctrine

The Armour Penetration characteristic of Pistol and melee weapons this model is equipped with is improved by 1 whilst this combat doctrine is active. For example, AP 0 becomes AP -1.

UPDATED WEAPONS AND DATASHEET AMENDMENTS

Since the release of *Codex: Blood Angels*, a number of weapons found in the book have had their profiles revised. Below you will find these profiles; these replace those found in the codex wherever they appear.

WEAPON	RANGE	TYPE	S	AP	D	ABILITIES
Auto bolt rifle	24"	Assault 3	4	0	1	-
Demolisher cannon	24"	Heavy D6	10	-3	D6	-
Flamestorm cannon	12"	Heavy D6	6	-2	2	When resolving an attack made with this weapon, do not make a hit roll: it automatically scores a hit.
Hand flamer	6"	Pistol D6	3	0	1	When resolving an attack made with this weapon, do not make a hit roll: it automatically scores a hit.
Icarus rocket pod	24"	Heavy D3	7	-1	2	When resolving an attack made with this weapon, add 1 to the hit roll if the target can **FLY**; otherwise subtract 1 from the hit roll.
Master-crafted auto bolt rifle	24"	Assault 3	4	0	2	-
Master-crafted stalker bolt rifle	36"	Heavy 1	4	-2	3	-
Stalker bolt rifle	36"	Heavy 1	4	-2	2	-

Datasheet Amendment: Reiver Squad

BLOOD ANGELS REIVER SQUADS (see *Codex: Blood Angels*) gain the **PHOBOS** keyword.

---

8 POWER	CHIEF LIBRARIAN MEPHISTON

NAME	M	WS	BS	S	T	W	A	Ld	Sv
Chief Librarian Mephiston	7"	2+	2+	5	5	6	5	9	2+

Chief Librarian Mephiston is a single model equipped with: plasma pistol; Vitarus; frag grenades; krak grenades. You can only include one of this model in your army.

WEAPON	RANGE	TYPE	S	AP	D	ABILITIES
Plasma pistol	When you choose this weapon to shoot with, select one of the profiles below.					
- Standard	12"	Pistol 1	7	-3	1	-
- Supercharge	12"	Pistol 1	8	-3	2	If any hit rolls of 1 are made for attacks with this weapon, the bearer is destroyed after shooting with this weapon.
Vitarus	Melee	Melee	x2	-3	D3	-
Frag grenades	6"	Grenade D6	3	0	1	-
Krak grenades	6"	Grenade 1	6	-1	D3	-

ABILITIES	**Angels of Death** (pg 34)
	Lord of Death: When this model would lose a wound, roll one D6; on a 5+ that wound is not lost.
	Psychic Hood: When a Deny the Witch test is taken for this model to resist a psychic power manifested by an enemy model within 12", add 1 to the total.
PSYKER	This model can attempt to manifest two psychic powers in your Psychic phase and attempt to deny two psychic powers in your opponent's Psychic phase. It knows *Smite* and three psychic powers from the Sanguinary discipline (see *Codex: Blood Angels*).
FACTION KEYWORDS	**IMPERIUM, ADEPTUS ASTARTES, BLOOD ANGELS**
KEYWORDS	**CHARACTER, INFANTRY, LIBRARIAN, PRIMARIS, PSYKER, CHIEF LIBRARIAN, MEPHISTON**

ASTORATH

NAME	M	WS	BS	S	T	W	A	Ld	Sv
Astorath	12"	2+	2+	4	4	5	4	9	2+

Astorath is a single model equipped with: bolt pistol; The Executioner's Axe; frag grenades; krak grenades. You can only include one of this model in your army.

WEAPON	RANGE	TYPE	S	AP	D	ABILITIES
Bolt pistol	12"	Pistol 1	4	0	1	-
The Executioner's Axe	Melee	Melee	+2	-3	D3	When resolving an attack made with this weapon, on a wound roll of 6+ this weapon has a Damage characteristic of 3.
Frag grenades	6"	Grenade D6	3	0	1	-
Krak grenades	6"	Grenade 1	6	-1	D3	-

ABILITIES	
	Angels of Death (pg 34) **Redeemer of the Lost:** Friendly **BLOOD ANGELS** units can use this model's Leadership instead of their own whilst they are within 6" of this model. In addition, when a Morale test is taken for a friendly **DEATH COMPANY** unit within 6" of this model, do not roll the dice; it is automatically passed. **Jump Pack Assault:** During deployment, you can set up this model high in the skies instead of setting it up on the battlefield. If you do, at the end of one of your Movement phases you can set up this model anywhere on the battlefield that is more than 9" away from enemy models. **Rosarius:** This model has a 4+ invulnerable save.	**Mass of Doom:** Once per battle, at the start of your Movement phase, this model can chant the Mass of Doom. Roll one D6 for each friendly **BLOOD ANGELS INFANTRY** unit within 6" of this model and apply the result below: **D6 Result** **1** **Frenzied Death Throes:** That unit suffers 1 mortal wound. **2-5** **Dark Wrath:** Until the end of the turn, when resolving an attack made with a melee weapon by a model in that unit, add 1 to the hit roll. **6** **Vessel of Sanguinius:** Until the end of the turn, models in that unit have a 4+ invulnerable save, and when resolving an attack made with a melee weapon by a model in that unit, add 1 to the hit roll.

PRIEST	This model knows the Litany of Hate (see below) and three other litanies from the Litanies of Battle (pg 58). At the start of the battle round, this model can recite two litanies it knows that have not already been recited by a friendly model that battle round. Roll one D6; on a 3+ the recited litany is inspiring and takes effect until the end of that battle round. **Litany of Hate:** If this litany is inspiring, you can re-roll hit rolls for attacks made with melee weapons by models in friendly **BLOOD ANGELS** units whilst their unit is within 6" of this model.

FACTION KEYWORDS	IMPERIUM, ADEPTUS ASTARTES, BLOOD ANGELS
KEYWORDS	CHARACTER, INFANTRY, CHAPLAIN, PRIEST, MASTER OF SANCTITY, JUMP PACK, FLY, ASTORATH

LEMARTES

NAME	M	WS	BS	S	T	W	A	Ld	Sv
Lemartes	12"	2+	3+	4	4	4	5	9	3+

Lemartes is a single model equipped with: bolt pistol; The Blood Crozius; frag grenades; krak grenades. You can only include one of this model in your army.

WEAPON	RANGE	TYPE	S	AP	D	ABILITIES
Bolt pistol	12"	Pistol 1	4	0	1	-
The Blood Crozius	Melee	Melee	+2	-2	D3	-
Frag grenades	6"	Grenade D6	3	0	1	-
Krak grenades	6"	Grenade 1	6	-1	D3	-

ABILITIES	Angels of Death (pg 34)	Jump Pack Assault: During deployment you can set up this model high in the skies instead of setting it up on the battlefield. If you do, at the end of one of your Movement phases you can set up this model anywhere on the battlefield that is more than 9" away from any enemy models.
	Fury Unbound: When a charge roll is made for a friendly **DEATH COMPANY** unit within 6" of this model, you can re-roll the dice. When resolving an attack made with a melee weapon by a model in a friendly **DEATH COMPANY** unit within 6" of this model, you can re-roll the hit roll.	
		Guardian of the Lost: Friendly **DEATH COMPANY** units can use this model's Leadership instead of their own whilst they are within 6" of this model.
	Rosarius: This model has a 4+ invulnerable save.	

PRIEST	This model knows the Litany of Hate (see below) and two other litanies from the Litanies of Battle (pg 58). At the start of the battle round, this model can recite one litany it knows that has not already been recited by a friendly model that battle round. Roll one D6; on a 3+ the recited litany is inspiring and takes effect until the end of that battle round. **Litany of Hate:** If this litany is inspiring, you can re-roll hit rolls for attacks made with melee weapons by models in friendly **BLOOD ANGELS** units whilst their unit is within 6" of this model.

FACTION KEYWORDS	IMPERIUM, ADEPTUS ASTARTES, BLOOD ANGELS, DEATH COMPANY
KEYWORDS	CHARACTER, INFANTRY, JUMP PACK, FLY, PRIEST, CHAPLAIN, LEMARTES

CHAPLAIN
IN TERMINATOR ARMOUR

NAME	M	WS	BS	S	T	W	A	Ld	Sv
Chaplain in Terminator Armour	5"	2+	3+	4	4	5	3	9	2+

A Chaplain in Terminator Armour is a single model equipped with: storm bolter; crozius arcanum.

WEAPON	RANGE	TYPE	S	AP	D	ABILITIES
Storm bolter	24"	Rapid Fire 2	4	0	1	-
Crozius arcanum	Melee	Melee	+1	-1	2	-

WARGEAR OPTIONS	• This model can be equipped with 1 item from the *Terminator Combi-weapons* list (see *Codex: Blood Angels*) instead of 1 storm bolter.

ABILITIES	Angels of Death (pg 34)	Teleport Strike: During deployment, you can set up this model in a teleportarium chamber instead of setting it up on the battlefield. If you do, at the end of one of your Movement phases you can set up this model anywhere on the battlefield that is more than 9" away from any enemy models.
	Spiritual Leaders: Friendly **BLOOD ANGELS** units can use this model's Leadership instead of their own whilst they are within 6" of this model.	
	Rosarius: This model has a 4+ invulnerable save.	

PRIEST	This model knows the Litany of Hate (see below) and two other litanies from the Litanies of Battle (pg 58). At the start of the battle round, this model can recite one litany it knows that has not already been recited by a friendly model that battle round. Roll one D6; on a 3+ the recited litany is inspiring and takes effect until the end of that battle round. **Litany of Hate:** If this litany is inspiring, you can re-roll hit rolls for attacks made with melee weapons by models in friendly **BLOOD ANGELS** units whilst their unit is within 6" of this model.

FACTION KEYWORDS	IMPERIUM, ADEPTUS ASTARTES, BLOOD ANGELS
KEYWORDS	CHARACTER, INFANTRY, PRIEST, TERMINATOR, CHAPLAIN

CHAPLAIN

NAME	M	WS	BS	S	T	W	A	Ld	Sv
Chaplain	6"	2+	3+	4	4	4	3	9	3+

A Chaplain is a single model equipped with: bolt pistol; crozius arcanum; frag grenades; krak grenades.

WEAPON	RANGE	TYPE	S	AP	D	ABILITIES
Bolt pistol	12"	Pistol 1	4	0	1	-
Crozius arcanum	Melee	Melee	+1	-1	2	-
Power fist	Melee	Melee	x2	-3	D3	When attacking with this weapon, you must subtract 1 from the hit roll.
Frag grenades	6"	Grenade D6	3	0	1	-
Krak grenades	6"	Grenade 1	6	-1	D3	-

WARGEAR OPTIONS	• This model can be equipped with one of the following instead of 1 bolt pistol: 1 boltgun; 1 power fist; 1 weapon from the *Combi-weapons* list (see *Codex: Blood Angels*); 1 weapon from the *Pistols* list (see *Codex: Blood Angels*). • This model can have a jump pack (**Power Rating +1**). If a model has a jump pack, it has a Move characteristic of 12" and gains the **FLY** and **JUMP PACK** keywords.

ABILITIES	Angels of Death (pg 34) Spiritual Leaders: Friendly **BLOOD ANGELS** units can use this model's Leadership instead of their own whilst they are within 6" of this model. Rosarius: This model has a 4+ invulnerable save.	Jump Pack Assault: If this model has a jump pack, then during deployment you can set up this model high in the skies instead of setting it up on the battlefield. If you do, at the end of one of your Movement phases you can set up this model anywhere on the battlefield that is more than 9" away from any enemy models.
PRIEST	This model knows the Litany of Hate (see below) and two other litanies from the Litanies of Battle (pg 58). At the start of the battle round, this model can recite one litany it knows that has not already been recited by a friendly model that battle round. Roll one D6; on a 3+ the recited litany is inspiring and takes effect until the end of that battle round. Litany of Hate: If this litany is inspiring, you can re-roll hit rolls for attacks made with melee weapons by models in friendly **BLOOD ANGELS** units whilst their unit is within 6" of this model.	
FACTION KEYWORDS	IMPERIUM, ADEPTUS ASTARTES, BLOOD ANGELS	
KEYWORDS	CHARACTER, INFANTRY, PRIEST, CHAPLAIN	

PRIMARIS CHAPLAIN

NAME	M	WS	BS	S	T	W	A	Ld	Sv
Primaris Chaplain	6"	2+	3+	4	4	5	4	9	3+

A Primaris Chaplain is a single model equipped with: absolvor bolt pistol; crozius arcanum; frag grenades; krak grenades.

WEAPON	RANGE	TYPE	S	AP	D	ABILITIES
Absolvor bolt pistol	16"	Pistol 1	5	-1	1	-
Crozius arcanum	Melee	Melee	+1	-1	2	-
Frag grenades	6"	Grenade D6	3	0	1	-
Krak grenades	6"	Grenade 1	6	-1	D3	-

ABILITIES	Angels of Death (pg 34) Rosarius: This model has a 4+ invulnerable save.	Spiritual Leaders: Friendly **BLOOD ANGELS** units can use this model's Leadership instead of their own whilst they are within 6" of this model.
PRIEST	This model knows the Litany of Hate (see below) and two other litanies from the Litanies of Battle (pg 58). At the start of the battle round, this model can recite one litany it knows that has not already been recited by a friendly model that battle round. Roll one D6; on a 3+ the recited litany is inspiring and takes effect until the end of that battle round. Litany of Hate: If this litany is inspiring, you can re-roll hit rolls for attacks made with melee weapons by models in friendly **BLOOD ANGELS** units whilst their unit is within 6" of this model.	
FACTION KEYWORDS	IMPERIUM, ADEPTUS ASTARTES, BLOOD ANGELS	
KEYWORDS	CHARACTER, INFANTRY, PRIMARIS, PRIEST, CHAPLAIN	

DEATH COMPANY INTERCESSORS

NAME	M	WS	BS	S	T	W	A	Ld	Sv
Death Company Intercessor	6"	3+	3+	4	4	2	2	7	3+

This unit contains 5 Death Company Intercessors. It can additionally contain up to 5 Death Company Intercessors (**Power Rating +5**). Every model is equipped with: bolt pistol; bolt rifle; frag grenades; krak grenades.

WEAPON	RANGE	TYPE	S	AP	D	ABILITIES
Auto bolt rifle	24"	Assault 3	4	0	1	-
Bolt pistol	12"	Pistol 1	4	0	1	-
Bolt rifle	30"	Rapid Fire 1	4	-1	1	-
Hand flamer	6"	Pistol D6	3	0	1	When resolving an attack made with this weapon, do not make a hit roll: it automatically scores a hit.
Stalker bolt rifle	36"	Heavy 1	4	-2	2	-
Chainsword	Melee	Melee	User	0	1	When the bearer fights, it makes 1 additional attack with this weapon.
Power fist	Melee	Melee	x2	-3	D3	When resolving an attack made with this weapon, subtract 1 from the hit roll.
Power sword	Melee	Melee	User	-3	1	-
Thunder hammer	Melee	Melee	x2	-3	3	When resolving an attack made with this weapon, subtract 1 from the hit roll.
Frag grenades	6"	Grenade D6	3	0	1	-
Krak grenades	6"	Grenade 1	6	-1	D3	-

WARGEAR OPTIONS	
	• Every model can be equipped with 1 auto bolt rifle instead of 1 bolt rifle.
	• Every model can be equipped with 1 stalker bolt rifle instead of 1 bolt rifle.
	• 1 model can:
	- Be equipped with one of the following in addition to their other weapons: 1 chainsword; 1 power fist; 1 power sword; 1 thunder hammer.
	- Be equipped with one of the following instead of their bolt rifle, auto bolt rifle or stalker bolt rifle: 1 chainsword; 1 hand flamer. A model cannot be equipped with 2 chainswords.
	• For every 5 models this unit contains, 1 model that is equipped with 1 bolt rifle, 1 auto bolt rifle or 1 stalker bolt rifle can have an auxiliary grenade launcher.

ABILITIES		
	Angels of Death (pg 34) **Auxiliary Grenade Launcher:** If a model has an auxiliary grenade launcher, Grenade weapons that model is equipped with have a Range characteristic of 30".	**Black Rage:** Add 1 to the Attacks characteristic of models in this unit during any turn in which it made a charge move. When a model in this unit would lose a wound, roll one D6; on a 6 that wound is not lost.

FACTION KEYWORDS	
	IMPERIUM, ADEPTUS ASTARTES, BLOOD ANGELS, DEATH COMPANY

KEYWORDS	
	INFANTRY, PRIMARIS, DEATH COMPANY INTERCESSORS

REPULSOR EXECUTIONER

DAMAGE
Some of this model's characteristics change as it suffers damage, as shown below:

REMAINING W	M	BS	A
9-16+	10"	3+	6
5-8	5"	4+	D6
1-4	3"	5+	1

NAME	M	WS	BS	S	T	W	A	Ld	Sv
Repulsor Executioner	*	6+	*	8	8	16	*	9	3+

A Repulsor Executioner is a single model equipped with: 2 fragstorm grenade launchers; heavy onslaught gatling cannon; macro plasma incinerator; 2 storm bolters; twin heavy bolter; twin Icarus ironhail heavy stubber. It has auto launchers.

WEAPON	RANGE	TYPE	S	AP	D	ABILITIES
Fragstorm grenade launcher	18"	Assault D6	4	0	1	-
Heavy laser destroyer	72"	Heavy 2	10	-4	D6	When resolving an attack made with this weapon, a damage roll of 1 or 2 counts as 3 instead.
Heavy onslaught gatling cannon	30"	Heavy 12	5	-1	1	-
Icarus rocket pod	24"	Heavy D3	7	-1	2	When resolving an attack made with this weapon, add 1 to the hit roll if the target can FLY; otherwise subtract 1 from the hit roll.
Ironhail heavy stubber	36"	Heavy 3	4	-1	1	-
Macro plasma incinerator	When you choose this weapon to shoot with, select one of the profiles below.					
- Standard	36"	Heavy D6	8	-4	1	-
- Supercharge	36"	Heavy D6	9	-4	2	For each hit roll of 1 made for attacks with this weapon, the bearer suffers 1 mortal wound after shooting this weapon.
Storm bolter	24"	Rapid Fire 2	4	0	1	-
Twin heavy bolter	36"	Heavy 6	5	-1	1	-
Twin Icarus ironhail heavy stubber	36"	Heavy 6	4	-1	1	When resolving an attack made with this weapon, add 1 to the hit roll if the target can FLY; otherwise subtract 1 from the hit roll.

WARGEAR OPTIONS	• This model can be equipped with 1 heavy laser destroyer instead of 1 macro plasma incinerator. • This model can additionally be equipped with 1 ironhail heavy stubber. • This model can additionally be equipped with 1 Icarus rocket pod.
ABILITIES	**Angels of Death** (pg 34) **Aquilon Optics:** If, in your Movement phase, this model does not move or moves a distance less than half its Move characteristic, it can shoot with its heavy laser destroyer or macro plasma incinerator twice in the following Shooting phase (the weapon must target the same unit both times). **Repulsor Field:** If any units with this ability are chosen as targets of a charge, subtract 2 from the charge roll. **Hover Tank:** Distances are always measured to and from this model's hull.
	Power of the Machine Spirit: This model does not suffer the penalty for moving and firing Heavy weapons. **Auto Launchers:** Instead of shooting in your Shooting phase, this model can use its auto launchers. Until the start of your next Shooting phase, when resolving an attack made with a ranged weapon against this model, subtract 1 from the hit roll. **Explodes:** When this model is destroyed, roll one D6 before any embarked models disembark and before removing it from play. On a 6 it explodes, and each unit within 6" suffers D6 mortal wounds.
TRANSPORT	This model has a transport capacity of 6 **BLOOD ANGELS PRIMARIS INFANTRY** models. Each **MK X GRAVIS** model takes up the space of 2 other models. It cannot transport **JUMP PACK** models.
FACTION KEYWORDS	**IMPERIUM, ADEPTUS ASTARTES, BLOOD ANGELS**
KEYWORDS	**VEHICLE, TRANSPORT, FLY, REPULSOR, REPULSOR EXECUTIONER**

CAPTAIN
IN PHOBOS ARMOUR

NAME	M	WS	BS	S	T	W	A	Ld	Sv
Captain in Phobos Armour	6"	2+	2+	4	4	6	5	9	3+

A Captain in Phobos Armour is a single model equipped with: bolt pistol; master-crafted instigator bolt carbine; combat knife; frag grenades; krak grenades. It has a camo cloak.

WEAPON	RANGE	TYPE	S	AP	D	ABILITIES
Bolt pistol	12"	Pistol 1	4	0	1	-
Master-crafted instigator bolt carbine	30"	Assault 1	4	-2	3	This weapon can target a **CHARACTER** unit even if it is not the closest enemy unit.
Combat knife	Melee	Melee	User	0	1	When the bearer fights, it makes 1 additional attack with this weapon.
Frag grenades	6"	Grenade D6	3	0	1	-
Krak grenades	6"	Grenade 1	6	-1	D3	-

ABILITIES	
Angels of Death (pg 34)	**Iron Halo:** This model has a 4+ invulnerable save.
Concealed Position: When you set up this model during deployment, it can be set up anywhere on the battlefield that is more than 9" away from the enemy deployment zone and any enemy models.	**Rites of Battle:** Re-roll hit rolls of 1 for attacks made by models in friendly **BLOOD ANGELS** units whilst their unit is within 6" of this model.
Omni-scrambler: Enemy units that are set up on the battlefield as reinforcements cannot be set up within 12" of this model.	**Camo Cloak:** When resolving an attack made with a ranged weapon against this model whilst it is receiving the benefit of cover, add 2 to the saving throw instead of 1.

FACTION KEYWORDS	**IMPERIUM, ADEPTUS ASTARTES, BLOOD ANGELS**
KEYWORDS	**CHARACTER, INFANTRY, PHOBOS, PRIMARIS, CAPTAIN**

LIBRARIAN
IN PHOBOS ARMOUR

NAME	M	WS	BS	S	T	W	A	Ld	Sv
Librarian in Phobos Armour	6"	3+	3+	4	4	5	4	9	3+

A Librarian in Phobos Armour is a single model equipped with: bolt pistol; force sword; frag grenades; krak grenades. It has a camo cloak.

WEAPON	RANGE	TYPE	S	AP	D	ABILITIES
Bolt pistol	12"	Pistol 1	4	0	1	-
Force sword	Melee	Melee	User	-3	D3	-
Frag grenades	6"	Grenade D6	3	0	1	-
Krak grenades	6"	Grenade 1	6	-1	D3	-

ABILITIES	Angels of Death (pg 34)	Camo Cloak: When resolving an attack made with a ranged weapon against this model whilst it is receiving the benefit of cover, add 2 to the saving throw instead of 1.
	Concealed Position: When you set up this model during deployment, it can be set up anywhere on the battlefield that is more than 9" away from the enemy deployment zone and any enemy models.	Psychic Hood: When a Deny the Witch test is taken for this model to resist a psychic power manifested by an enemy model within 12", add 1 to the total.

PSYKER	This model can attempt to manifest two psychic powers in your Psychic phase and attempt to deny one psychic power in your opponent's Psychic phase. It knows *Smite* and two psychic powers from the Obscuration discipline (pg 57).

FACTION KEYWORDS	IMPERIUM, ADEPTUS ASTARTES, BLOOD ANGELS
KEYWORDS	CHARACTER, INFANTRY, PHOBOS, PRIMARIS, PSYKER, LIBRARIAN

SANGUINARY PRIEST

NAME	M	WS	BS	S	T	W	A	Ld	Sv
Sanguinary Priest	6"	2+	3+	4	4	4	3	9	3+

A Sanguinary Priest is a single model equipped with: bolt pistol; chainsword; frag grenades; krak grenades.

WEAPON	RANGE	TYPE	S	AP	D	ABILITIES
Bolt pistol	12"	Pistol 1	4	0	1	-
Boltgun	24"	Rapid Fire 1	4	0	1	-
Chainsword	Melee	Melee	User	0	1	When the bearer fights, it makes 1 additional attack with this weapon.
Frag grenades	6"	Grenade D6	3	0	1	-
Krak grenades	6"	Grenade 1	6	-1	D3	-

WARGEAR OPTIONS	• This model may take a jump pack (**Power Rating +1**). If it does, its Move characteristic is increased to 12" and it gains the JUMP PACK and FLY keywords.

ABILITIES	And They Shall Know No Fear (pg 34)	Narthecium: At the end of your Movement phase, this model can provide medical attention to one friendly BLOOD ANGELS INFANTRY or BLOOD ANGELS BIKER unit within 3" of it. If that unit contains a model that has lost any wounds, that model regains up to D3 lost wounds. Otherwise, if any models from that unit have been destroyed, roll one D6; on a 4+ you can return one destroyed model from that unit to the battlefield with 1 wound remaining, placing it within 3" of this model and in unit coherency (if the model cannot be placed in this way, it is not returned to the battlefield). On a 3 or less, this model cannot shoot, charge or fight this turn as it recovers the gene-seed of the fallen warrior. Each unit can only be provided medical attention once per turn.
	Blood Chalice: Add 1 to the Strength characteristic of models in friendly BLOOD ANGELS INFANTRY and BLOOD ANGELS BIKER units whilst their unit is within 6" of any SANGUINARY PRIEST models.	
	Jump Pack Assault: If this model has a jump pack, then during deployment you can set up this unit high in the skies instead of setting it up on the battlefield. If you do, at the end of one of your Movement phases you can set up this unit anywhere on the battlefield that is more than 9" away from any enemy models.	

FACTION KEYWORDS	IMPERIUM, ADEPTUS ASTARTES, BLOOD ANGELS
KEYWORDS	CHARACTER, INFANTRY, SANGUINARY PRIEST

LIEUTENANTS
IN PHOBOS ARMOUR

NAME	M	WS	BS	S	T	W	A	Ld	Sv
Lieutenant in Phobos Armour	6"	2+	3+	4	4	5	4	8	3+

This unit contains 1 Lieutenant in Phobos Armour. It can additionally contain 1 Lieutenant in Phobos Armour (**Power Rating +4**). Every model is equipped with: bolt pistol; master-crafted occulus bolt carbine; paired combat blades; frag grenades; krak grenades. Every model has a grav-chute.

WEAPON	RANGE	TYPE	S	AP	D	ABILITIES
Bolt pistol	12"	Pistol 1	4	0	1	-
Heavy bolt pistol	12"	Pistol 1	4	-1	1	-
Master-crafted occulus bolt carbine	24"	Rapid Fire 1	4	0	2	When resolving an attack made with this weapon, the target does not receive the benefit of cover to its saving throw.
Combat knife	Melee	Melee	User	0	1	When the bearer fights, it makes 1 additional attack with this weapon.
Paired combat blades	Melee	Melee	User	0	1	When resolving an attack made with this weapon, an unmodified hit roll of 6 scores 2 hits instead of 1.
Frag grenades	6"	Grenade D6	3	0	1	-
Krak grenades	6"	Grenade 1	6	-1	D3	-

WARGEAR OPTIONS	• Any model can be equipped with 1 heavy bolt pistol and 1 combat knife instead of 1 master-crafted occulus bolt carbine, 1 paired combat blades and 1 bolt pistol. If it is, it has smoke grenades instead of a grav-chute and gains the **REIVER** keyword.

ABILITIES	**Angels of Death** (pg 34)	**Company Heroes:** During deployment, every model in this unit must be set up at the same time, though they do not need to be set up in unit coherency. From that point onwards, each model is treated as a separate unit.
	Grav-chute: If this model has a grav-chute, then during deployment you can set up this model in low altitude instead of setting it up on the battlefield. If you do, at the end of one of your Movement phases you can set up this model anywhere on the battlefield that is more than 9" away from any enemy models.	**Smoke Grenades:** If this model has smoke grenades, then once per battle, instead of shooting in your Shooting phase, it can use its smoke grenades. Until the start of your next Shooting phase, when resolving an attack made with a ranged weapon against this model, subtract 1 from the hit roll.
	Terror Troops: Whilst any **REIVER** units from your army are within 3" of any enemy units, subtract 1 from the Leadership characteristic of each of those enemy units for each **REIVER** unit from your army that is within 3" of that enemy unit (to a maximum of -3).	**Tactical Precision:** Re-roll wound rolls of 1 for attacks made by models in friendly **BLOOD ANGELS** units whilst their unit is within 6" of this model.

FACTION KEYWORDS	**IMPERIUM, ADEPTUS ASTARTES, BLOOD ANGELS**
KEYWORDS	**CHARACTER, INFANTRY, PHOBOS, PRIMARIS, LIEUTENANTS**

'They cannot hide from us, slink and skulk as they might. We can sense the minutest change in ambient temperature and perceive the transpectral residue of their xenos bodies.

We have lost many brave warriors to this menace, but their feeding stops here, now! Make each shot count, brothers. Shatter their skulls if they dare sneak from their holes. Master your rage, until we fall upon them and then slick your blades in their blood.'

- Brother Goriel,
10th Company Incursor

INTERCESSOR SQUAD

NAME	M	WS	BS	S	T	W	A	Ld	Sv
Intercessor	6"	3+	3+	4	4	2	2	7	3+
Intercessor Sergeant	6"	3+	3+	4	4	2	3	8	3+

This unit contains 1 Intercessor Sergeant and 4 Intercessors. It can additionally contain up to 5 Intercessors (**Power Rating +5**). Every model is equipped with: bolt pistol; bolt rifle; frag grenades; krak grenades.

WEAPON	RANGE	TYPE	S	AP	D	ABILITIES
Auto bolt rifle	24"	Assault 3	4	0	1	-
Bolt pistol	12"	Pistol 1	4	0	1	-
Bolt rifle	30"	Rapid Fire 1	4	-1	1	-
Hand flamer	6"	Pistol D6	3	0	1	When resolving an attack made with this weapon, do not make a hit roll: it automatically scores a hit.
Stalker bolt rifle	36"	Heavy 1	4	-2	2	-
Chainsword	Melee	Melee	User	0	1	When the bearer fights, it makes 1 additional attack with this weapon.
Power fist	Melee	Melee	x2	-3	D3	When resolving an attack made with this weapon, subtract 1 from the hit roll.
Power sword	Melee	Melee	User	-3	1	-
Thunder hammer	Melee	Melee	x2	-3	3	When resolving an attack made with this weapon, subtract 1 from the hit roll.
Frag grenades	6"	Grenade D6	3	0	1	-
Krak grenades	6"	Grenade 1	6	-1	D3	-

WARGEAR OPTIONS	
	• Every model can be equipped with 1 auto bolt rifle instead of 1 bolt rifle.
	• Every model can be equipped with 1 stalker bolt rifle instead of 1 bolt rifle.
	• The Intercessor Sergeant can be equipped with one of the following instead of 1 bolt rifle, 1 auto bolt rifle or 1 stalker bolt rifle: 1 chainsword; 1 hand flamer.
	• If the Intercessor Sergeant is not equipped with 1 chainsword, it can additionally be equipped with one of the following: 1 chainsword; 1 power fist; 1 power sword; 1 thunder hammer.
	• For every 5 models this unit contains, 1 model that is equipped with 1 bolt rifle, 1 auto bolt rifle or 1 stalker bolt rifle can have an auxiliary grenade launcher.

ABILITIES	
	Angels of Death (pg 34) **Combat Squads:** If this unit contains 10 models, then during deployment, before any units have been set up, it can be divided into two units of 5 models.
	Auxiliary Grenade Launcher: If a model has an auxiliary grenade launcher, Grenade weapons that model is equipped with have a Range characteristic of 30".

FACTION KEYWORDS	IMPERIUM, ADEPTUS ASTARTES, BLOOD ANGELS
KEYWORDS	INFANTRY, PRIMARIS, INTERCESSOR SQUAD

Intercessor Sergeant with chainsword and bolt pistol

Intercessors with bolt rifles

INFILTRATOR SQUAD

NAME	M	WS	BS	S	T	W	A	Ld	Sv
Infiltrator	6"	3+	3+	4	4	2	2	7	3+
Infiltrator Helix Adept	6"	3+	3+	4	4	2	2	7	3+
Infiltrator Sergeant	6"	3+	3+	4	4	2	3	8	3+

This unit contains 1 Infiltrator Sergeant and 4 Infiltrators. It can additionally contain up to 5 Infiltrators (**Power Rating +5**). It can contain 1 Infiltrator Helix Adept instead of 1 Infiltrator. Every model is equipped with: bolt pistol; marksman bolt carbine; frag grenades; krak grenades. Every model has smoke grenades.

WEAPON	RANGE	TYPE	S	AP	D	ABILITIES
Bolt pistol	12"	Pistol 1	4	0	1	-
Marksman bolt carbine	24"	Rapid Fire 1	4	0	1	When resolving an attack made with this weapon, an unmodified hit roll of 6 automatically scores a hit and successfully wounds the target (do not make a wound roll).
Frag grenades	6"	Grenade D6	3	0	1	-
Krak grenades	6"	Grenade 1	6	-1	D3	-

WARGEAR OPTIONS	• If this unit does not contain 1 Infiltrator Helix Adept, 1 Infiltrator can additionally have an Infiltrator comms array.

ABILITIES	**Angels of Death** (pg 34) **Concealed Positions:** When you set up this unit during deployment, it can be set up anywhere on the battlefield that is more than 9" away from the enemy deployment zone and any enemy models. **Helix Adept:** At the end of your Movement phase, this unit's Infiltrator Helix Adept can provide medical attention to this unit. If this unit contains any models that have lost any wounds, select one of those models to regain 1 lost wound. Otherwise, if any models from this unit have been destroyed, roll one D6; on a 5+ you can return one destroyed model from this unit to the battlefield with 1 wound remaining, placing it within 3" of this unit's Infiltrator Helix Adept and in unit coherency (if the model cannot be placed in this way, it is not returned to the battlefield). On a 4 or less, this unit's Infiltrator Helix Adept cannot shoot this turn as it recovers the gene-seed of the fallen warrior. Each unit can only be provided medical attention once per turn.	**Combat Squads:** If this unit contains 10 models, then during deployment, before any units have been set up, it can be divided into two units of 5 models. **Omni-scramblers:** Enemy units that are set up on the battlefield as reinforcements cannot be set up within 12" of this unit. **Smoke Grenades:** Once per battle, instead of shooting in your Shooting phase, this unit can use its smoke grenades. Until the start of your next Shooting phase, when resolving an attack made with a ranged weapon against this unit, subtract 1 from the hit roll. **Infiltrator Comms Array:** Whilst this unit contains a model with an Infiltrator comms array, if there are any friendly **Blood Angels Phobos Captain** or **Blood Angels Phobos Lieutenant** models on the battlefield, this unit is always treated as being within range of those models' Rites of Battle and Tactical Precision abilities.

FACTION KEYWORDS	**Imperium, Adeptus Astartes, Blood Angels**
KEYWORDS	**Infantry, Phobos, Primaris, Infiltrator Squad**

INCURSOR SQUAD

NAME	M	WS	BS	S	T	W	A	Ld	Sv
Incursor	6"	3+	3+	4	4	2	2	7	3+
Incursor Sergeant	6"	3+	3+	4	4	2	3	8	3+

This unit contains 1 Incursor Sergeant and 4 Incursors. It can additionally contain up to 5 Incursors (**Power Rating +5**). Every model is equipped with: bolt pistol; occulus bolt carbine; paired combat blades; frag grenades; krak grenades. Every model has smoke grenades.

WEAPON	RANGE	TYPE	S	AP	D	ABILITIES
Bolt pistol	12"	Pistol 1	4	0	1	-
Occulus bolt carbine	24"	Rapid Fire 1	4	0	1	When resolving an attack made with this weapon, the target does not receive the benefit of cover to its saving throw.
Paired combat blades	Melee	Melee	User	0	1	When resolving an attack made with this weapon, an unmodified hit roll of 6 scores 2 hits instead of 1.
Frag grenades	6"	Grenade D6	3	0	1	-
Krak grenades	6"	Grenade 1	6	-1	D3	-

WARGEAR OPTIONS	• 1 Incursor can additionally have a haywire mine.

ABILITIES	**Angels of Death** (pg 34)	**Combat Squads:** If this unit contains 10 models, then during deployment, before any units have been set up, it can be divided into two units of 5 models.

Haywire Mine: In your Movement phase, one model from your army with a haywire mine that has not been primed can prime it. At any point during that model's move, place one Primed Haywire Mine within 1" of it, more than 3" away from any enemy models and more than 6" away from any other Primed Haywire Mines. If an enemy unit moves within 3" of that Primed Haywire Mine, roll one D6; on a 2+ that enemy unit suffers D3 mortal wounds. If that unit is a **VEHICLE**, it suffers D3+1 mortal wounds instead. That Primed Haywire Mine is then removed from play.

The Primed Haywire Mine is represented by the Primed Haywire Mine model, but does not count as a model for any rules purposes.

Concealed Positions: When you set up this unit during deployment, it can be set up anywhere on the battlefield that is more than 9" away from the enemy deployment zone and any enemy models.

Multi-spectrum array: When resolving an attack made with a ranged weapon by a model in this unit, ignore hit roll modifiers and Ballistic Skill modifiers.

Smoke Grenades: Once per battle, instead of shooting in your Shooting phase, this unit can use its smoke grenades. Until the start of your next Shooting phase, when resolving an attack made with a ranged weapon against this unit, subtract 1 from the hit roll.

FACTION KEYWORDS	**IMPERIUM, ADEPTUS ASTARTES, BLOOD ANGELS**
KEYWORDS	**INFANTRY, PHOBOS, PRIMARIS, INCURSOR SQUAD**

INVICTOR TACTICAL WARSUIT

NAME	M	WS	BS	S	T	W	A	Ld	Sv
Invictor Tactical Warsuit	*	*	*	7	6	13	4	8	3+

DAMAGE
Some of this model's characteristics change as it suffers damage, as shown below:

REMAINING W	M	WS	BS
7-13+	10"	3+	3+
4-6	8"	4+	4+
1-3	6"	5+	5+

An Invictor Tactical Warsuit is a single model equipped with: fragstorm grenade launcher; heavy bolter; incendium cannon; 2 ironhail heavy stubbers; Invictor fist.

WEAPON	RANGE	TYPE	S	AP	D	ABILITIES
Fragstorm grenade launcher	18"	Assault D6	4	0	1	-
Heavy bolter	36"	Heavy 3	5	-1	1	-
Incendium cannon	12"	Heavy 2D6	5	-1	1	When resolving an attack made with this weapon, do not make a hit roll: it automatically scores a hit.
Ironhail heavy stubber	36"	Heavy 3	4	-1	1	-
Twin ironhail autocannon	48"	Heavy 6	7	-1	2	-
Invictor fist	Melee	Melee	x2	-3	3	-

WARGEAR OPTIONS	• This model can be equipped with 1 twin ironhail autocannon instead of 1 incendium cannon.

ABILITIES	**Angels of Death** (pg 34)

Explodes: When this model is destroyed, roll one D6 before removing it from play. On a 6 it explodes, and each unit within 6" suffers D6 mortal wounds.

Concealed Position: When you set up this model during deployment, it can be set up anywhere on the battlefield that is more than 9" away from the enemy deployment zone and any enemy models.

Heavy Sidearm: Whilst this model is within 1" of any enemy units, its heavy bolter has a Type characteristic of Pistol 3.

FACTION KEYWORDS	IMPERIUM, ADEPTUS ASTARTES, BLOOD ANGELS
KEYWORDS	VEHICLE, INVICTOR TACTICAL WARSUIT

SUPPRESSOR SQUAD

NAME	M	WS	BS	S	T	W	A	Ld	Sv
Suppressor	12"	3+	3+	4	4	2	2	7	3+
Suppressor Sergeant	12"	3+	3+	4	4	2	3	8	3+

This unit contains 1 Suppressor Sergeant and 2 Suppressors. Every model is equipped with: accelerator autocannon; bolt pistol; frag grenades; krak grenades. Every model has a grav-chute.

WEAPON	RANGE	TYPE	S	AP	D	ABILITIES
Accelerator autocannon	48"	Heavy 2	7	-2	2	-
Bolt pistol	12"	Pistol 1	4	0	1	-
Frag grenades	6"	Grenade D6	3	0	1	-
Krak grenades	6"	Grenade 1	6	-1	D3	-

ABILITIES	**Angels of Death** (pg 34)

Grav-chute: During deployment, you can set up this unit in low altitude instead of setting it up on the battlefield. If you do, at the end of one of your Movement phases you can set up this unit anywhere on the battlefield that is more than 9" away from any enemy models.

Smoke Launcher: Once per battle, instead of shooting in your Shooting phase, this unit's Suppressor Sergeant can use his smoke launcher. Until the start of your next Shooting phase, when resolving an attack made with a ranged weapon against this unit, subtract 1 from the hit roll.

Suppressing Fire: If an enemy model is destroyed as a result of an attack made with an accelerator autocannon by a model in this unit, that enemy model's unit cannot fire Overwatch this turn.

FACTION KEYWORDS	IMPERIUM, ADEPTUS ASTARTES, BLOOD ANGELS
KEYWORDS	INFANTRY, JUMP PACK, PRIMARIS, FLY, SUPPRESSOR SQUAD

ELIMINATOR SQUAD

NAME	M	WS	BS	S	T	W	A	Ld	Sv
Eliminator	6"	3+	3+	4	4	2	2	7	3+
Eliminator Sergeant	6"	3+	3+	4	4	2	3	8	3+

This unit contains 1 Eliminator Sergeant and 2 Eliminators. Every model is equipped with: bolt pistol; bolt sniper rifle; frag grenades; krak grenades. Every model has a camo cloak.

WEAPON	RANGE	TYPE	S	AP	D	ABILITIES
Bolt pistol	12"	Pistol 1	4	0	1	-
Bolt sniper rifle	When you choose this weapon to shoot with, select one of the profiles below.					
- Executioner round	36"	Heavy 1	5	-1	1	This weapon can target units that are not visible to the bearer, and can target a **CHARACTER** unit even if it is not the closest enemy unit. When resolving an attack made with this weapon, add 2 to the hit roll, and the target does not receive the benefit of cover to its saving throw.
- Hyperfrag round	36"	Heavy D3	5	0	1	This weapon can target a **CHARACTER** unit even if it is not the closest enemy unit.
- Mortis round	36"	Heavy 1	5	-2	D3	This weapon can target a **CHARACTER** unit even if it is not the closest enemy unit. When resolving an attack made with this weapon, a wound roll of 6+ inflicts 1 mortal wound on the target in addition to any other damage.
Instigator bolt carbine	24"	Assault 1	4	-1	2	This weapon can target a **CHARACTER** even if it is not the closest enemy unit.
Las fusil	36"	Heavy 1	8	-3	3	-
Frag grenades	6"	Grenade D6	3	0	1	-
Krak grenades	6"	Grenade 1	6	-1	D3	-

WARGEAR OPTIONS	• The Eliminator Sergeant can be equipped with one of the following instead of 1 bolt sniper rifle: 1 instigator bolt carbine, 1 las fusil. • Every Eliminator can be equipped with 1 las fusil instead of 1 bolt sniper rifle.

ABILITIES	**Angels of Death** (pg 34) **Camo Cloak:** When resolving an attack made with a ranged weapon against a model in this unit whilst it is receiving the benefit of cover, add 2 to the saving throw instead of 1. **Guided Aim:** Instead of shooting in your Shooting phase, this unit's Eliminator Sergeant can guide his squad's aim. Until the end of that phase, when resolving an attack made with a ranged weapon by a model in this unit, add 1 to the hit roll and wound roll.	**Covering Fire:** The first time this unit's Eliminator Sergeant fires Overwatch with an instigator bolt carbine in your opponent's turn, this unit can, after it has resolved its Overwatch, move as if it were your Movement phase (it cannot Advance as part of this move). **Concealed Positions:** When you set up this unit during deployment, it can be set up anywhere on the battlefield that is more than 9" away from the enemy deployment zone and any enemy models.

FACTION KEYWORDS	**IMPERIUM, ADEPTUS ASTARTES, BLOOD ANGELS**
KEYWORDS	**INFANTRY, PHOBOS, PRIMARIS, ELIMINATOR SQUAD**

IMPULSOR

NAME	M	WS	BS	S	T	W	A	Ld	Sv
Impulsor	*	6+	*	7	7	11	*	8	3+

An Impulsor is a single model equipped with: 2 storm bolters.

DAMAGE

Some of this model's characteristics change as it suffers damage, as shown below:

REMAINING W	M	BS	A
6-11+	14"	3+	3
3-5	7"	4+	D3
1-2	4"	5+	1

WEAPON	RANGE	TYPE	S	AP	D	ABILITIES
Bellicatus missile array	When you choose this weapon to shoot with, select one of the profiles below.					
- Krak missiles	48"	Heavy 1	8	-2	D6	-
- Frag missiles	48"	Heavy D6	4	0	1	-
- Icarus missiles	48"	Heavy D3	7	-1	D3	When resolving an attack made with this weapon, add 1 to the hit roll if the target can **Fly**; otherwise subtract 1 from the hit roll.
Fragstorm grenade launcher	18"	Assault D6	4	0	1	-
Ironhail heavy stubber	36"	Heavy 3	4	-1	1	-
Ironhail skytalon array	36"	Heavy 6	4	-1	1	When resolving an attack made with this weapon, add 1 to the hit roll and 1 to the wound roll if the target can **Fly**; otherwise subtract 1 from the hit roll.
Storm bolter	24"	Rapid Fire 2	4	0	1	-

WARGEAR OPTIONS	• This model can additionally be equipped with 1 ironhail heavy stubber. • This model can be equipped with 2 fragstorm grenade launchers instead of 2 storm bolters. • This model can have a shield dome or an orbital comms array, or can be equipped with one of the following: 1 bellicatus missile array, 1 ironhail skytalon array.

ABILITIES	**Angels of Death** (pg 34) **Hover Tank:** Distances are always measured to and from this model's hull. **Repulsor Field:** If any units with this ability are chosen as targets of a charge, subtract 2 from the charge roll. **Assault Vehicle:** After this model moves in your Movement phase, if this model did not Advance, any units embarked aboard it can disembark. Units that do so cannot be chosen to charge with that turn. **Shield Dome:** A model with a shield dome has a 4+ invulnerable save.	**Orbital Comms Array:** In your Shooting phase, one model from your army with an orbital comms array that has not been used can use it to call in an orbital barrage. If it does, select one point on the battlefield and roll one D6 for each unit within D6" of that point, subtracting 1 from the result if the unit being rolled for is a **Character**. On a 4+ the unit being rolled for suffers D3 mortal wounds. **Explodes:** When this model is destroyed, roll one D6 before any embarked models disembark and before removing it from play. On a 6 it explodes, and each unit within 6" suffers D6 mortal wounds.

TRANSPORT	This model has a transport capacity of 6 **Blood Angels Primaris Infantry** models. It cannot transport **Jump Pack** or **Mk X Gravis** models.
FACTION KEYWORDS	**Imperium, Adeptus Astartes, Blood Angels**
KEYWORDS	**Vehicle, Transport, Fly, Impulsor**

'Swift and deadly do the sons of Baal strike. We are as the rad storm in the desert, sweeping down upon all in its path and leaving nothing but corpses in our wake. Aboard steeds of adamant we shall fall upon our foes and drive them before us unto their absoute ruin. This do I swear, upon the blood of the Primarch and the honour of Baal. Now, brothers, prepare to attack!'

- Brother-Captain Raphaelos, Oath of Moment before the Sharavos Cleansing

THE COLOURS OF DEATH

Fighting on multiple fronts throughout the wider War Zone Baal, the Blood Angels sought to stem the flow of the xenos tide. Chief Librarian Mephiston fought in several conflicts, some missions known only to Commander Dante and a select cadre of elite warriors. On the eve of many battles, individual Intercessors were among those who fell to the curse of the Black Rage.

Chief Librarian Mephiston

Death Company Intercessor with bolt pistol and chainsword

Death Company Intercessor with auto bolt rifle

Death Company Intercessor with auto bolt rifle

Death Company Intercessor with auto bolt rifle and auxiliary grenade launcher

Death Company Intercessor with auto bolt rifle

Lieutenant in Phobos Armour with master-crafted occulus bolt carbine

SONS OF SANGUINIUS

In this section you'll find additional rules for Battle-forged armies that include BLOOD ANGELS Detachments and Blood Angels successor Chapter Detachments – that is, Detachments that only include BLOOD ANGELS units or units drawn from the same Blood Angels successor Chapter respectively. These include new Warlord Traits, Stratagems, Relics and psychic powers that help to reflect the tactics used by the sons of Sanguinius on the battlefield.

ABILITIES

All units (excluding SERVITORS) in BLOOD ANGELS Detachments and Blood Angels successor Chapter Detachments (other than Super-heavy Auxiliary Detachments) gain the Red Thirst ability, and all Troops units in such Detachments gain the Defenders of Humanity ability (see *Codex: Blood Angels*). In addition, if your army is Battle-forged, all units from your army with the Combat Doctrines ability gain the Savage Echoes ability, so long as every unit from your army (with the exception of those that are UNALIGNED) is a BLOOD ANGELS unit or every unit from your army is from the same Blood Angels successor Chapter.

SAVAGE ECHOES

The shock assaults of the Blood Angels are legendary, their warriors never halting for an instant, never allowing the enemy to recover. Though few outside the Chapter realise it, this is the Blood Angels as they really are, the suppression of their bloodlust lifted for but an instant.

Whilst the Assault Doctrine is active, if a unit with this ability makes a charge move, is charged or performs a Heroic Intervention, add 1 to the Attacks characteristic of models in that unit until the end of the turn (note that this is cumulative with the bonus these models receive from the Shock Assault ability).

THE RED THIRST

When resolving an attack made with a melee weapon by a model with this ability in a turn in which that model's unit made a charge move, was charged or performed a Heroic Intervention, add 1 to the wound roll. When a unit with this ability Advances or makes a charge move, add 1 to the Advance roll or charge roll.

SUCCESSOR CHAPTERS

The following rules apply to units drawn from Blood Angels successor Chapters:

Warlord Traits

If your Warlord is a CHARACTER model from a Blood Angels successor Chapter, you can use the Blood Angels Warlord Traits table (see *Codex: Blood Angels*) or the Vanguard Warlord Traits table opposite to determine what Warlord Trait they have. Replace the BLOOD ANGELS keyword in all instances in that Warlord Trait (if any) with your Warlord's <CHAPTER> keyword. FLESH TEARERS Warlords instead have access to the Flesh Tearers Warlord Traits (pg 62).

Relics of Baal

Blood Angels successor Chapters have access to the Special-issue Wargear Relics (pg 60); Relics of Baal cannot be given to a CHARACTER model from a successor Chapter unless you use the Honoured by Baal Stratagem (pg 55).

Stratagems

All units from Blood Angels successor Chapters are considered to have the BLOOD ANGELS keyword for the purpose of using Blood Angels Stratagems.

Psychic Powers

LIBRARIAN models from Blood Angels successor Chapters can know psychic powers from the Sanguinary discipline (see *Codex: Blood Angels*) and the Obscuration discipline (pg 57) in the same manner as LIBRARIAN models in BLOOD ANGELS Detachments. When such a model uses one of these psychic powers, replace the BLOOD ANGELS keyword in all instances on that power (if any) with that model's successor Chapter keyword.

Litanies

CHAPLAINS from Blood Angels successor Chapters can know litanies from the Litanies of Battle table (pg 58). When such a model uses one of these litanies, replace the BLOOD ANGELS keyword in all instances on that litany (if any) with your CHAPLAIN's successor Chapter keyword.

Tactical Objectives

Units from Blood Angels successor Chapters are considered to have the BLOOD ANGELS keyword for the purposes of using Blood Angels Tactical Objectives (see *Codex: Blood Angels*).

VANGUARD WARLORD TRAITS

The Phobos-armoured commanders of the Blood Angels coordinate everything from single-squad missions to entire Vanguard armies. Combining the strength and grace of true sons of Sanguinius with the subtlety, precision and stealth of the Vanguard, these leaders can outmanoeuvre any enemy.

If a **BLOOD ANGELS PHOBOS CHARACTER** model is your Warlord, you can use the Vanguard Warlord Traits table below to determine what Warlord Trait they have instead of the Warlord Traits table from *Codex: Blood Angels*.

1 SHOOT AND FADE

This warrior harries the foe before returning to the shadows.

At the start of your Shooting phase, you can select one friendly **BLOOD ANGELS PHOBOS** unit within 6" of this Warlord. After shooting with that unit, it can move as if it were your Movement phase; if it does, it must Advance and cannot declare a charge in the following Charge phase.

2 LORD OF DECEIT

This leader is adept at subterfuge and spreading misinformation.

At the start of the first battle round, before the first turn begins, select up to three friendly **BLOOD ANGELS PHOBOS** units on the battlefield. Remove them from the battlefield and set them up again as described in the Deployment section of the mission (if both players have abilities that redeploy units, roll off; the winner chooses who redeploys their units first).

3 MASTER OF THE VANGUARD

This Space Marine is a living legend of the Vanguard formations, and an inspiration to his battle-brothers.

Add 1" to the Move characteristic of friendly **BLOOD ANGELS PHOBOS** units whilst they are within 6" of this Warlord. Add 1 to Advance rolls and charge rolls made for friendly **BLOOD ANGELS PHOBOS** units whilst they are within 6" of this Warlord.

4 STEALTH ADEPT

So masterfully does this warlord slip through enemy territory that he appears to the foe as little more than a spectre.

When resolving an attack made against this Warlord, subtract 1 from the hit roll.

5 TARGET PRIORITY

This tactician is constantly seeking prime targets.

At the start of your Shooting phase, select one friendly **BLOOD ANGELS PHOBOS** unit within 3" of this Warlord; until the end of that phase, when resolving an attack made with a ranged weapon by a model in that unit, add 1 to the hit roll.

6 MARKSMAN'S HONOURS

This warlord is one of the finest sharpshooters in the galaxy.

Add 1 to the Damage characteristic of ranged weapons this Warlord is equipped with. This does not apply to Grenades or Relics.

STRATAGEMS

If your army is Battle-forged and includes any BLOOD ANGELS Detachments (excluding Auxiliary Support Detachments), you have access to the Stratagems shown here, and can spend Command Points to activate them. These reflect the unique strategies used by the Blood Angels on the battlefield.

DUTY ETERNAL
1CP

Blood Angels Stratagem

Having tasted death before, the Dreadnought pilot is determined to do his duty before his end finally comes.

Use this Stratagem when a **BLOOD ANGELS DREADNOUGHT** model from your army is chosen as the target for an attack. Until the end of the phase, when resolving an attack made against that model, halve the damage inflicted (rounding up).

VETERAN INTERCESSORS
1/2CP

Blood Angels Stratagem

This squad has been noted for exemplary service.

Use this Stratagem before the battle. Select one **BLOOD ANGELS INTERCESSOR SQUAD** unit from your army that contains 5 models for 1 Command Point or one **BLOOD ANGELS INTERCESSOR SQUAD** unit from your army that contains 6 or more models for 2 Command Points. Add 1 to the Attacks and Leadership characteristics of models in that unit. Each **INTERCESSOR SQUAD** unit can only be selected for this Stratagem once per battle.

MASTERFUL MARKSMANSHIP
1CP

Blood Angels Stratagem

Sternguard are experts at exploiting the foe's weaknesses.

Use this Stratagem when a **BLOOD ANGELS STERNGUARD VETERAN SQUAD** unit from your army fires Overwatch or is chosen to shoot with. Until the end of the phase, when resolving an attack made with a special issue boltgun by a model in that unit, add 1 to the wound roll.

FURY OF THE FIRST
1CP

Blood Angels Stratagem

When the fighting is at its fiercest, the Terminators of the Blood Angels truly show their quality.

Use this Stratagem in any phase. Select one **BLOOD ANGELS TERMINATOR** unit from your army. Until the end of that phase, when resolving an attack made by a model in that unit, add 1 to the hit roll.

HUNTER-SLAYER MISSILE
1CP

Blood Angels Stratagem

Hunter-slayer missiles eliminate priority targets.

Use this Stratagem in your Shooting phase. Select one **BLOOD ANGELS REPULSOR** model from your army to launch a hunter-slayer missile, then select one enemy **VEHICLE** unit or **MONSTER** unit within 48" of that model that is not within 1" of any units from your army. Roll one D6; if the result is equal to or greater than that model's Ballistic Skill, that unit suffers D3 mortal wounds. Each **REPULSOR** model can only be selected for this Stratagem once per battle.

RAPID FIRE
2CP

Blood Angels Stratagem

The combination of post-human reflexes and rigid bolter-drills produce a devastating rate of blistering firepower.

Use this Stratagem at the start of your Shooting phase. Select one **BLOOD ANGELS INTERCESSOR SQUAD** or **DEATH COMPANY INTERCESSORS** unit from your army. Until the end of that phase, bolt rifles that models in that unit are equipped with have a Type characteristic of Rapid Fire 2.

BIG GUNS NEVER TIRE
1CP

Blood Angels Stratagem

None can stay the Blood Angels' armoured wrath.

Use this Stratagem when a **BLOOD ANGELS VEHICLE** unit from your army is chosen to shoot with in your Shooting phase. Until the end of that phase, that unit does not suffer the penalty for moving and firing Heavy weapons.

VISAGE OF THE DAMNED
1CP

Blood Angels Stratagem

The enemy are beset by visions of their own mortality.

Use this Stratagem in the Fight phase. Select one **BLOOD ANGELS** unit from your army that has the Death Mask ability. Until the end of the phase, when resolving an attack against that unit, subtract 1 from the hit roll.

HERO OF THE CHAPTER
1CP
Blood Angels Stratagem

Every Space Marine is a champion in their own right, a warrior-god who stands between Mankind and darkness.

Use this Stratagem before the battle, after nominating your Warlord. Select one **BLOOD ANGELS CHARACTER** model from your army that is not your Warlord and determine one Warlord Trait for it; it is regarded as your Warlord for the purposes of that Warlord Trait. Each Warlord Trait in your army must be unique (if randomly generated, re-roll duplicate results). You can only use this Stratagem once per battle.

TRANSHUMAN PHYSIOLOGY
2CP
Blood Angels Stratagem

The legacy of a Primarch flows through the Blood Angels' veins, allowing them to overcome grievous wounds.

Use this Stratagem when a **BLOOD ANGELS** unit from your army that is not a **VEHICLE** or a **SERVITOR** is chosen as the target of an attack. Until the end of the phase, when resolving an attack made against that unit, an unmodified wound roll of 1-3 always fails, irrespective of any abilities that the weapon or the model making that attack may have.

VENGEANCE OF THE MACHINE SPIRIT
2CP
Blood Angels Stratagem

The raging machine spirit wreaks havoc on the enemy.

Use this Stratagem when a **BLOOD ANGELS LAND RAIDER** model, **BLOOD ANGELS REPULSOR** model or **BLOOD ANGELS STORMRAVEN GUNSHIP** model from your army is destroyed. That model can either automatically explode (do not roll a D6), shoot with one of its ranged weapons as if it were your Shooting phase, or make one attack with one of its melee weapons as if it were the Fight phase (use the top row of that model's damage table when resolving these attacks).

REFUSAL TO DIE
1CP
Blood Angels Stratagem

Only the direst wounds penetrate the darkest madness.

Use this Stratagem in any phase, after a **DEATH COMPANY** unit from your army is chosen as the target of an attack. Until the end of that phase, when a model in that unit would lose a wound, roll one D6; on a 5+ that wound is not lost. You can only use this Stratagem once per turn.

STEADY ADVANCE
1CP
Blood Angels Stratagem

Blood Angels pour a stream of fire into their foes as they advance unrelentingly.

Use this Stratagem in your Shooting phase, when a **BLOOD ANGELS INFANTRY** unit from your army is chosen to shoot with. Until the end of that phase, for the purposes of the Bolter Discipline ability, that unit is treated as if it had remained stationary in your previous Movement phase.

HONOURED BY BAAL
1CP
Blood Angels Stratagem

It is not unheard of for the relics of the Blood Angels to be bestowed for a time upon a worthy successor Chapter.

Use this Stratagem after nominating a model drawn from a Blood Angels successor Chapter to be your Warlord. You can give one Relic of Baal (see page 59 and *Codex: Blood Angels*) to a **CHARACTER** model from your army that is drawn from a Blood Angels successor Chapter instead of giving them a Special-issue Wargear Relic (pg 60). If you do, replace the **BLOOD ANGELS** keyword in all instances on that Relic (if any) with that model's successor Chapter keyword. You can only use this Stratagem once per battle.

HAMMER OF WRATH
1CP
Blood Angels Stratagem

Launching themselves into the enemy ranks, the Blood Angels crash home with bone-breaking force.

Use this Stratagem when a **BLOOD ANGELS JUMP PACK** unit from your army finishes a charge move. For each model in that unit, you can select one enemy unit within 1" of that model and roll one D6; on a 5+ that enemy unit suffers 1 mortal wound.

DEATH ON THE WIND
1CP
Blood Angels Stratagem

The crackling disruptor fields of encarmine weapons reflect in gilded armour before striking down their wielders' enemies.

Use this Stratagem in the Fight phase. Select one **SANGUINARY GUARD** unit from your army. Until the end of the phase, when resolving an attack made by a model in that unit, treat a damage result of 1 as 2.

TARGET SIGHTED

3CP

Blood Angels Stratagem

With pinpoint accuracy, Intercessors pick out enemy commanders, as well as their armour's weak points.

Use this Stratagem at the start of your Shooting phase. Select one **BLOOD ANGELS INTERCESSOR SQUAD** or **DEATH COMPANY INTERCESSORS** unit from your army. Until the end of that phase, stalker bolt rifles that models in that unit are equipped with gain the following ability: 'This weapon can target a **CHARACTER** unit even if it is not the closest enemy unit. When resolving an attack made with this weapon, a wound roll of 6+ inflicts 1 mortal wound on the target in addition to any other damage.'

UNBRIDLED ARDOUR

1CP

Blood Angels Stratagem

To their brothers' defence, Blood Angels will fly instantly.

Use this Stratagem in the Charge phase. Select one **BLOOD ANGELS** unit from your army. That unit can perform a Heroic Intervention as if it were a **CHARACTER**. In addition, that unit can perform a Heroic Intervention if there are any enemy units within 6" of them instead of 3", and when doing so can move up to 6" instead of 3".

ADAPTIVE STRATEGY

1CP

Blood Angels Stratagem

The Blood Angels are adept at fluidly altering their strategy on the wing.

Use this Stratagem at the start of the battle round if there are any **BLOOD ANGELS CHARACTER** models from your army on the battlefield, before you change which combat doctrine is active. If the Assault Doctrine is currently active, you can change it so that the Tactical Doctrine is now active. Alternatively, if the Tactical Doctrine is currently active, you can change it so that the Devastator Doctrine is now active. You can only use this Stratagem once per battle.

BOLTSTORM

2CP

Blood Angels Stratagem

The sons of Baal unleash an inescapable hail of fire.

Use this Stratagem at the start of your Shooting phase. Select one **BLOOD ANGELS INTERCESSOR SQUAD** or **DEATH COMPANY INTERCESSORS** unit from your army. Until the end of that phase, auto bolt rifles that models in that unit are equipped with gain the following ability: 'When resolving an attack made with this weapon against a target that is within half range, do not make a hit roll: it automatically scores a hit.'

EXPLOSIVE JUDGEMENT

1CP

Blood Angels Stratagem

When golden fire blazes from on high, none can hide.

Use this Stratagem in your Shooting phase. Select one **SANGUINARY GUARD** unit from your army. Until the end of the phase, when resolving an attack made with an angelus boltgun by a model in that unit, you can re-roll the wound roll and the target does not receive the benefit of cover to its saving throw.

GENE-WROUGHT MIGHT

1CP

Blood Angels Stratagem

Primaris Blood Angels can deliver devastating blows, their strength deriving from arcane bio-tech.

Use this Stratagem in the Fight phase, when a **BLOOD ANGELS PRIMARIS INFANTRY** unit from your army is chosen to fight with. Until the end of that phase, when resolving an attack made with a melee weapon by a model in that unit, an unmodified hit roll of 6 automatically scores a hit and successfully wounds the target (do not make a wound roll).

CHALICE OVERFLOWING

1CP

Blood Angels Stratagem

The Sanguinary Priesthood know that one drop of their Primarch's blood allowed to fall is one too many.

Use this Stratagem in your Movement phase. Select one **SANGUINARY PRIEST** unit from your army. Until the end of the turn, that unit can use its Narthecium ability one additional time. In addition, this unit can target a friendly unit with its Narthecium ability even if that unit has already been targeted by the Narthecium ability earlier that turn.

OBSCURATION DISCIPLINE

Those Space Marine Librarians seconded to Vanguard operations are trained in the psychic arts of obscuration and illusion. They weave impenetrable cloaks of warp energy around their battle-brothers, conjure haunting visions to distract and terrify their foes, and ease the Vanguard formations' passage through enemy territory.

Before the battle, generate the psychic powers for **BLOOD ANGELS PSYKER** models that know powers from the Obscuration discipline using the table below. You can either roll one D6 to generate each power randomly (re-rolling duplicate results), or you can select which powers the psyker knows.

1 SHROUDING

The psyker uses his mastery of the warp to fog the minds of his enemies, clouding their senses so that his allies appear as indistinct shadows.

Shrouding has a warp charge value of 6. If manifested, select one friendly **BLOOD ANGELS PHOBOS** unit within 18" of this psyker. Until the start of your next Psychic phase, enemy models can only shoot that unit if it is the closest target that is visible to them or they are firing Overwatch.

2 SOUL SIGHT

The psyker shares his warp-sight with his brethren, causing their eyes to glow with an ethereal light. So empowered, no foe can escape their omniscient gaze; the souls of their targets flare like flaming beacons in the dark.

Soul Sight has a warp charge value of 6. If manifested, select one friendly **BLOOD ANGELS PHOBOS** unit within 18" of this psyker. Until the start of your next Psychic phase, when resolving an attack made with a ranged weapon by a model in that unit, you can re- roll the hit roll and the target does not receive the benefit of cover to its saving throw.

3 MIND RAID

The psyker peers into the mind of the foe, raiding their thoughts for secret codes, battle plans, the location of hidden forces and any other tactical information that might be useful. Such brute psychic interrogation doubtless inflicts severe cerebral trauma on its victim.

Mind Raid has a warp charge value of 6. If manifested, select one enemy model within 18" of and visible to this psyker. That model's unit suffers 1 mortal wound. If your army is Battle-forged and that model is a **CHARACTER**, roll 3D6; if the result is equal to or greater than that model's Leadership characteristic, you gain 1 Command Point.

4 HALLUCINATION

The psyker instils terror in his foes by conjuring nightmarish images out of their memories.

Hallucination has a warp charge value of 6. If manifested, select one enemy unit within 18" of and visible to this psyker. Until the start of your next Psychic phase, subtract 1 from the Leadership characteristic of models in that unit. Your opponent then rolls 2D6; if the result is greater than the highest Leadership characteristic of models in that unit, then until the start of your next Psychic phase, when resolving an attack made by a model in that unit, subtract 1 from the hit roll.

5 TENEBROUS CURSE

The psyker sends a psychic bolt lancing through his foes' minds. As they reel from the assault, their own shadows drag down their casters.

Tenebrous Curse has a warp charge value of 6. If manifested, select one enemy unit that cannot **FLY** and is within 18" of and visible to this psyker. That unit suffers 1 mortal wound and, until the start of your next Psychic phase, halve that unit's Move characteristic and the result of any Advance rolls and charge rolls made for it (rounding up).

6 TEMPORAL CORRIDOR

The psyker creates an invisible corridor in which the passage of time is altered, allowing his allies to rapidly traverse the battlefield.

Temporal Corridor has a warp charge value of 7. If manifested, select one friendly **BLOOD ANGELS PHOBOS** unit within 3" of this psyker. That unit can immediately move as if it were your Movement phase, but it cannot Fall Back as part of this move and must Advance. When the Advance roll is made for that Advance, roll 3D6 and discard two of the results. You cannot use Temporal Corridor on the same unit more than once per Psychic phase.

LITANIES OF BATTLE

Space Marine Chaplains are exemplars of righteous wrath. Powerful orators and accomplished warriors both, they provide bellicose counsel to their comrades and act as spiritual bastions for their Chapter. The litanies that Chaplains intone on the battlefield imbue those around them with fresh determination and martial fury.

Before the battle, generate the litanies for **BLOOD ANGELS CHAPLAIN** models that know litanies from the Litanies of Battle using the table below. You can either roll one D6 to generate each litany randomly (re-rolling duplicate results), or you can select which litanies the model knows. In addition, if your army is Battle-forged, **CHAPLAINS** in **BLOOD ANGELS** Detachments know the Invocation of Destruction litany in addition to any others they know.

1. LITANY OF FAITH
The Chaplain exhorts his charges to steel themselves against even the most dangerous weapons the enemy can bring to bear.

If this litany is inspiring, then when a model in a friendly **BLOOD ANGELS** unit within 6" of this model would lose a wound as a result of a mortal wound, roll one D6; on a 5+ that wound is not lost. This is not cumulative with any similar rules (e.g. the Standard of Sacrifice Relic).

2. CATECHISM OF FIRE
The Chaplain calls upon his brothers to unleash a relentless storm of close-range firepower.

If this litany is inspiring, select one friendly **BLOOD ANGELS** unit within 6" of this model. When resolving an attack made with a ranged weapon by a model in that unit against the closest visible enemy unit to that model, add 1 to the wound roll.

3. EXHORTATION OF RAGE
The Chaplain bellows his fury at the enemy, his brothers surging forwards to strike them down.

If this litany is inspiring, select one friendly **BLOOD ANGELS** unit within 6" of this model. When resolving an attack made with a melee weapon by a model in that unit, on an unmodified hit roll of 6 you can make one additional attack against the same unit using the same weapon. This additional attack cannot generate another attack.

4. MANTRA OF STRENGTH
The Chaplain focuses his mind on the purity of the blood that runs through his veins, bestowed upon him by the Primarch himself.

If this litany is inspiring, add 1 to this model's Attacks and Strength characteristics and add 1 to the Damage characteristic of melee weapons this model is equipped with.

5. RECITATION OF FOCUS
The Chaplain recites creeds that focus the minds of his brothers to ensure their shots strike true.

If this litany is inspiring, select one friendly **BLOOD ANGELS** unit within 6" of this model. When resolving an attack made with a ranged weapon by a model in that unit, add 1 to the hit roll.

6. CANTICLE OF HATE
Bellowing his hatred of the foe, the Chaplain leads his brothers in the wholesale destruction of the enemy.

If this litany is inspiring, add 2 to charge rolls made for friendly **BLOOD ANGELS** units whilst they are within 6" of this model. In addition, when a friendly **BLOOD ANGELS** unit makes a pile-in or consolidate move within 6" of this model, models in that unit can move up to an additional 3". This is not cumulative with any other ability that adds to a unit's charge roll or increases the distance it can pile in or consolidate.

BLOOD ANGELS: INVOCATION OF DESTRUCTION
Recalling from legend the deeds of Azkaellon, the Chaplain inspires his battle-brothers to still their souls, compelling their blades to strike true and deep.

If this litany is inspiring, select one friendly **BLOOD ANGELS** unit within 6" of this model. When resolving an attack made with a melee weapon by a model in that unit, on an unmodified wound roll of 6, that weapon has an Armour Penetration characteristic of -4 for that attack.

RELICS OF BAAL

Within the Blood Angels' fortress-monastery, the Arx Angelicum, lie treasured relics of great artifice. Some of unknown provenance, others whose legends are told across the galaxy, they are bestowed as rare honours upon the Chapter's champions. Together, artefact and warrior win yet more bloody victories.

If your army is led by a **BLOOD ANGELS** Warlord, you can give one of the following Relics of Baal to a **BLOOD ANGELS CHARACTER** model from your army instead of giving them a Relic from *Codex: Blood Angels*. Named characters (such as Brother Corbulo) cannot be given the following Relics.

Note that some Relics are weapons that replace one of the model's existing weapons. Where this is the case, you must, if you are using points values, still pay the cost of the weapon that is being replaced. Write down any Relics your models have on your army roster.

DECIMATOR

This exquisite rifle unleashes an unending storm of fire. Decimator's recoil dampers and the twinned machine spirits overseeing its cyclic mechanisms are the result of decades (and lives) expended in the bowels of Mars' forge temples, while each individually crafted shell is inscribed with the Versus Decimatus from the Codex Astartes.

Model with master-crafted auto bolt rifle only. This Relic replaces a master-crafted auto bolt rifle and has the following profile:

WEAPON	RANGE	TYPE	S	AP	D
Decimator	24"	Assault 3	5	-2	2

Abilities: When resolving an attack made with this weapon, the bearer does not suffer the penalty for Advancing and firing Assault weapons.

WRATH OF BAAL

If this ancient banner was ever known by another name, it has long been lost to time. All surviving records refer to it only as the Wrath of Baal, for that is what its presence heralds. Where it flies, its depiction of Sanguinius framed by his angelic wings spurs his sons to leap further and higher. The teardrops of polished bloodstone remind them of their Primarch's and Chapter's sacrifice, and so they burn their jump packs hard, the swifter to bring the retribution of the Blood Angels down upon their foes.

SANGUINARY ANCIENT model only. At the start of your Movement phase, add 2 to the Move characteristic of models in friendly **BLOOD ANGELS JUMP PACK** units if their unit is within 6" of this model. This bonus lasts until the end of the turn.

BIOMANTIC SARCOPHAGUS

This casket projects and refines the mind of the Librarian interred within a Dreadnought chassis. Psychically sensitive filaments are threaded throughout, while wafer stacks are installed beneath the Librarian's biological remains, each a shaving of the crystalline material found accreting in Geller field cores. Dangerously cascading energies are siphoned through the crystal wafers, while the Librarian's powers are channelled along every arcane angle of the Sarcophagus' psychic architecture.

LIBRARIAN DREADNOUGHT model only. Add 6" to the range of the psychic powers this model manifests from the Sanguinary discipline (see *Codex: Blood Angels*). In addition, once per turn, when a Psychic test or Deny the Witch test is taken for this model, you can re-roll one of the dice.

FIGURE OF DEATH

Chaplain Umbrael served with the Chapter over two millennia ago. His bombastic sermons, amplified through vox units in his armour, accompanied a visceral aura of dread around the black-clad warrior. Umbrael's sculpted crozius arcanum, the Figure of Death, became so infused with the fear he embodied – so it is claimed – that to face a Chaplain wielding it today is to face terror itself.

Model with crozius arcanum only. This Relic replaces a crozius arcanum and has the following profile:

WEAPON	RANGE	TYPE	S	AP	D
Figure of Death	Melee	Melee	+1	-2	2

Abilities: When resolving an attack made with this weapon, on a successful wound roll the target is terrified until the end of the turn in addition to any normal damage. Whilst a unit is terrified, subtract 2 from the Leadership characteristic of models in that unit.

GLEAMING PINIONS

Light glints from the Gleaming Pinions' curves, whether the wan light of stars or garish explosions. Appearing as merely beautifully sculpted wings adorning the bearer's jump pack, this unique artefact contains hundreds of micro-servos connected to individual ceramite feathers and planar surfaces. With such aerodynamic control, the wearer can twist and bank at incredible speeds, turning heavenward soars into stooping dives in a heartbeat.

JUMP PACK model only. This model can charge in a turn in which it Fell Back. In addition, when a charge roll is made for this model, add 1 to the result.

SPECIAL-ISSUE WARGEAR

Many are the prized artefacts and legendary weapons kept within the vaults of the Blood Angels and their successor Chapters. Those who can trace their lineage to Sanguinius have always evinced an aesthetic appreciation of sculpted refinement and many of their relics radiate as much beauty as they do death.

If your army is led by a **Blood Angels** Warlord or a Warlord drawn from a Blood Angels successor Chapter (pg 52), you can give one of the following Special-issue Wargear Relics to a **Blood Angels Character** model from your army, or a **Character** model from your army that is drawn from a Blood Angels successor Chapter, instead of giving them a Relic from *Codex: Blood Angels*. These are considered to be Relics of Baal for all rules purposes. Named characters and **Vehicles** cannot be given any of the following Relics.

Note that some Relics are weapons that replace one of the model's existing weapons. Where this is the case, you must, if you are using points values, still pay the cost of the weapon that is being replaced. Write down any Relics your models have on your army roster.

ADAMANTINE MANTLE

These flowing cloaks sometimes incorporate the shrouds that have lain over the tombs of Chapter heroes. The wearer is filled with the strength of their forebear in their hour of need, thus enduring the most grievous of wounds.

When a model with this Relic would lose a wound, roll one D6; on a 5+ that wound is not lost.

ARTIFICER ARMOUR

The sons of Sanguinius possess some of the most wondrous suits of armour in the Imperium. These ornately sculpted assemblages of engraved plate provide superior protection and afford a fluid ease of movement. All who set eyes upon the wearer are left in no doubt of their nobility and grace.

A model with this Relic has a Save characteristic of 2+ and a 5+ invulnerable save.

QUAKE BOLTS

Each quake bolt is crafted individually by a Magos of the Adeptus Mechanicus, and contains a warhead that emits a pulsed shock wave. Anyone caught in the vicinity is thrown from their feet and becomes easy prey for assault units.

When you give a model this Relic, select one bolt weapon (pg 34) that model is equipped with. When that model is chosen to shoot with, you can choose for that weapon to fire a quake bolt. If you do, you can only make one attack with that weapon, but if a hit is scored, the target is felled until the end of the turn and the attack sequence continues. When resolving an attack made with a melee weapon against a felled unit, add 1 to the hit roll.

MASTER-CRAFTED WEAPON

The finest artificers of the Chapter forge weapons of utter lethality for their angelic battle-brothers to wield in battle. To be granted the use of one is indeed a high honour.

When you give a model this Relic, select one weapon that model is equipped with (this cannot be a weapon whose profile includes the word 'master-crafted'). Add 1 to the Damage characteristic of that weapon. That weapon is considered to be a Relic of Baal.

DIGITAL WEAPONS

Digital weapons are concealed lasers fitted into bionic implants or power-armoured gauntlets. Short-ranged and powerful, they can be triggered in the midst of melee to blast the enemy point-blank with angelic retribution.

When a model with this Relic fights, it can make 1 additional attack using the close combat weapon profile (see the *Warhammer 40,000* Rulebook). When resolving that attack, if a hit is scored the target suffers 1 mortal wound and the attack sequence ends.

FLESHRENDER GRENADES

These-red spheres contain small servo-automata ringed with multiple circular gyro-saws like miniature astrolabes. They follow limited logic paths to rend and tear anything nearby in fountains of blood before their power runs out.

Model with frag grenades only. This Relic replaces frag grenades and has the following profile:

WEAPON	RANGE	TYPE	S	AP	D
Fleshrender Grenades	6"	Grenade 3	5	-3	2

Abilities: When resolving an attack made with this weapon, the target does not receive the benefit of cover to its saving throw.

ICON OF THE ANGEL

Entrusted to one whose faith in the Primogenitor is profound and articulate, each Icon of the Angel takes a unique form. Whether a token chained to a vambrace or a small shrine upon the bearer's backpack, all are a unique representation of Sanguinius. The bearer reminds his brothers of the heretics who fled after laying low the Angel, exhorting them to let no enemy escape their grasp again.

When a charge roll is made for a friendly **Blood Angels** unit or unit with the same successor Chapter keyword as a model with this Relic whilst within 3" of that model, you can re-roll any of the dice.

FLESH TEARERS

This section presents the rules for fielding an army formed from the Flesh Tearers Chapter, a Blood Angels successor Chapter. If your army is Battle-forged and includes any FLESH TEARERS Detachments, the rules in this section can be used in addition to those presented in *Codex: Blood Angels*.

ABILITIES

If your army is Battle-forged, all units (excluding SERVITORS) in FLESH TEARERS Detachments (other than Super-heavy Auxiliary Detachments) gain the Fury Within ability, instead of The Red Thirst ability.

Fury Within

The Flesh Tearers labour under a bloodthirsty recklessness. When controlled and focussed, however, this murderous ferocity can make them unstoppable.

When resolving an attack made with a melee weapon by a model with this ability in a turn in which that model's unit made a charge move, was charged or performed a Heroic Intervention, add 1 to the wound roll. In addition, when resolving an attack made with a melee weapon by a model in this unit, on an unmodified wound roll of 6 improve that weapon's Armour Penetration characteristic by 1 for that attack (e.g. AP 0 becomes AP -1).

WARLORD TRAITS

If a FLESH TEARERS CHARACTER is your Warlord, you can use the Warlord Traits table below to determine what Warlord Trait they have. You can either roll one D3 to randomly generate one, or you can select one.

1 MERCILESS BUTCHER

The warlord is but a single, blood-fulled moment away from succumbing to the Black Rage. In battle they are lost to the pursuit of slaughter, hacking apart all before them with unrelenting savagery.

When this Warlord is chosen to fight in the Fight phase, they can make 1 additional attack with one of its melee weapons for every 5 enemy models within 3" of it, to a maximum of 3 additional attacks.

2 OF WRATH AND RAGE

With snarls of hate and a bellow of rage the warlord fires the blood of his brothers, reminding them of the vengeance owed to a universe that saw Sanguinius laid low.

When resolving an attack made with a melee weapon by this Warlord, on an unmodified hit roll of 6 you can make 1 additional attack against the same unit using the same weapon. This additional attack cannot generate another attack.

3 CRETACIAN BORN

To survive on the death world of Cretacia, a hunter must be swifter than the murderous beasts around him. A son of this brutal world, the warlord acts with ferocious swiftness, rushing into combat before his prey has time to react.

Overwatch attacks cannot be made against this Warlord.

NAMED CHARACTERS

If the following character is your Warlord, they must have the associated Warlord Trait shown below:

CHARACTER	WARLORD TRAIT
Gabriel Seth	Merciless Butcher

STRATAGEMS

If your army is Battle-forged and includes any **Flesh Tearers** Detachments (excluding Auxiliary Support Detachments), you have access to the Stratagems shown here, and can spend Command Points to activate them. These reflect the unique strategies used by the Flesh Tearers on the battlefield.

SAVAGE DESTRUCTION
2CP

Flesh Tearers Stratagem

The Flesh Tearers' enemies are not merely killed, but rent apart in fountains of bloody gore.

Use this Stratagem at the start of the Fight phase. Select one enemy unit. Until the end of the turn, when a model in that unit is destroyed as a result of an attack made by a **Flesh Tearers** model from your army, that destroyed model counts as two destroyed models for the purpose of any Morale test taken for that unit.

AGGRESSIVE ONSLAUGHT
1CP

Flesh Tearers Stratagem

With a need to slay, Flesh Tearers constantly push forward towards new foes.

Use this Stratagem in your Fight phase. Select one **Flesh Tearers Infantry** unit from your army. Until the end of the phase, when models in that unit make a pile-in move, they can move up to 6" instead of 3".

RELICS OF CRETACIA

If your army is led by a **Flesh Tearers** Warlord, you can give one of the following Relics of Cretacia to a **Flesh Tearers Character** model in your army instead of giving them a Relic from *Codex: Blood Angels*. Named characters (such as Gabriel Seth) cannot be given any of the following Relics.

Note that some Relics are weapons that replace one of the model's existing weapons. Where this is the case, you must, if you are using points values, still pay the cost of the weapon that is being replaced. Write down any Relics your models have on your army roster.

SEVERER OF THREADS

This monstrous chainsword has ended the fates of countless enemies of the Imperium. Tyrants, tainted war engines, hideous xenos; all have felt its twin rows of blurring teeth.

Model with chainsword only. This Relic replaces a chainsword and has the following profile:

WEAPON	RANGE	TYPE	S	AP	D
Severer of Threads	Melee	Melee	+1	-1	1

Abilities: When the bearer fights, it makes D3 additional attacks with this weapon. When resolving an attack made with this weapon against an **Infantry** unit, an unmodified wound roll of 6 inflicts 1 mortal wound on the target in addition to any other damage.

SORROW'S GENESIS

The Flesh Tearers' Sanguinary Priesthood view this elder narthecium as one of their deadliest weapons. From its scalpels and unguents rises a fallen Flesh Tearer, ready to inflict bloody retribution upon the enemy for his wounds.

Sanguinary Priest, Primaris Apothecary or **Sanguinary Novitiate** model only. A model with this Relic loses the Narthecium ability and has the following ability :

'**Sorrow's Genesis:** At the end of your Movement phase, this model can provide medical attention to one friendly **Flesh Tearers Infantry** or **Flesh Tearers Biker** unit within 3". If that unit contains any models that have lost any wounds, select one of those models to regain up to 3 lost wounds. Otherwise, if any models from that unit have been destroyed, roll one D6; on a 2+ you can return one destroyed model from that unit to the battlefield with 3 lost wounds regained, placing it within 3" of this model and in unit coherency (if the model cannot be placed in this way, it is not returned to the battlefield). Each unit can only be affected by the Sorrow's Genesis or Narthecium abilities once per turn.'

NAME GENERATOR

If you wish to randomly generate a name for one of your Blood Angels warriors, you can roll a D66 and consult one or both of the tables below. To roll a D66, simply roll two D6, one after the other – the first represents tens and the second represents digits, giving you a result between 11 and 66.

D66	FORENAME
11	Cezare
12	Amareus
13	Kaerladeo
14	Corphal
15	Erasmus
16	Daenor
21	Tyborel
22	Rafael
23	Zorael
24	Niccolasa
25	Morlaeo
26	Mariano
31	Tuomanni
32	Leonid
33	Sevrael
34	Chiorre
35	Faustian
36	Rubio
41	Lukar
42	Donatelus
43	Kaerel
44	Aldus
45	Raelyn
46	Anchronus
51	Semartes
52	Nicodemus
53	Arca
54	Fontaeus
55	Furian
56	Mataneo
61	Vitrian
62	Arteino
63	Martellos
64	Lucien
65	Raldaeo
66	Marzio

D66	SURNAME
11	Aphael
12	Varseus
13	Metraen
14	Belarius
15	Oras
16	Athenos
21	Seraphan
22	Variano
23	Bardella
24	Moriar
25	Nassio
26	Maratio
31	Raneil
32	Comaeus
33	Spiccare
34	Castivar
35	Sanzeo
36	Antraeon
41	Arteros
42	Tybael
43	Vennaro
44	Redolpho
45	Vesta
46	Traviola
51	Lorenso
52	Urrel
53	Maschio
54	Amuto
55	Goriel
56	Messaro
61	Rephas
62	Furio
63	Ravini
64	Forell
65	Gallani
66	Bodonne

POINTS VALUES

If you are playing a matched play game, or a game that uses a points limit, you can use the following lists to determine the total points cost of your army. Simply add together the points values of all your models, as well as the wargear they are equipped with, to determine your army's total points value.

HQ

UNIT	MODELS PER UNIT	POINTS PER MODEL (Excluding wargear)
Captain	1	74
Captain in Cataphractii Armour	1	95
Captain in Gravis Armour	1	90
Captain in Phobos Armour	1	90
Captain in Terminator Armour	1	95
Captain with Jump Pack	1	93
Chaplain	1	72
Chaplain in Terminator Armour	1	90
Chaplain with Jump Pack	1	90
Land Raider Excelsior	1	200
Librarian	1	80
Librarian Dreadnought	1	110
Librarian in Phobos Armour	1	90
Librarian in Terminator Armour	1	100
Librarian with Jump Pack	1	108
Lieutenants	1-2	60
Lieutenants in Phobos Armour	1-2	75
Lieutenants with Jump Packs	1-2	78
Primaris Captain	1	78
Primaris Chaplain	1	77
Primaris Librarian	1	90
Primaris Lieutenants	1-2	65
Rhino Primaris	1	70
Sanguinary Priest	1	60
Sanguinary Priest with Jump Pack	1	70
Techmarine	1	45

NAMED CHARACTERS

UNIT	MODELS PER UNIT	POINTS PER MODEL (Including wargear)
Astorath	1	105
Brother Corbulo	1	83
Captain Tycho	1	85
Chief Librarian Mephiston	1	145
Commander Dante	1	150
Gabriel Seth	1	110
Lemartes	1	100
The Sanguinor	1	130
Tycho the Lost	1	70

TROOPS

UNIT	MODELS PER UNIT	POINTS PER MODEL (Excluding wargear)
Incursor Squad	5-10	19
Infiltrator Squad	5-10	22 (Infiltrator Helix Adept is 32)
Intercessor Squad	5-10	17
Scout Squad	5-10	11
Tactical Squad	5-10	12

ELITES

UNIT	MODELS PER UNIT	POINTS PER MODEL (Excluding wargear)
Aggressor Squad	3-6	21
Cataphractii Terminator Squad	5-10	26
Company Ancient	1	63
Company Champion	1	40
Company Veterans	2-5	14
Contemptor Dreadnought	1	88
Death Company	5-15	15
Death Company with Jump Packs	5-15	18
Death Company Dreadnought	1	70
Death Company Intercessors	5-10	18
Dreadnought	1	60
Invictor Tactical Warsuit	1	90
Furioso Dreadnought	1	60
Primaris Ancient	1	69
Primaris Apothecary	1	60
Redemptor Dreadnought	1	105
Reiver Squad	5-10	16
Sanguinary Ancient	1	55
Sanguinary Guard	4-10	20
Sanguinary Novitiate	1	50
Servitors	4	5
Sternguard Veteran Squad	5-10	14
Tartaros Terminator Squad	5-10	23
Terminator Ancient	1	87
Terminator Assault Squad	5-10	23
Terminator Squad	5-10	23
Vanguard Veteran Squad	5-10	14
Vanguard Veteran Squad with Jump Packs	5-10	17

FAST ATTACK

UNIT	MODELS PER UNIT	POINTS PER MODEL (Excluding wargear)
Assault Squad	5-10	12
Assault Squad with Jump Packs	5-10	15
Attack Bike Squad	1-3	25
Bike Squad	3-8	21
- Attack Bike	0-1	25
Inceptor Squad	3-6	25
Land Speeders	1-3	45
Scout Bike Squad	3-9	21
Suppressor Squad	3	18

HEAVY SUPPORT

UNIT	MODELS PER UNIT	POINTS PER MODEL (Excluding wargear)
Baal Predator	1	90
Devastator Squad	5-10	13
- Armorium Cherub	-	5
Eliminator Squad	3	18
Hellblaster Squad	5-10	18
Hunter	1	75
Land Raider	1	180
Land Raider Crusader	1	200
Land Raider Redeemer	1	180
Predator	1	85
Repulsor Executioner	1	215
Stalker	1	75
Vindicator	1	125
Whirlwind	1	65

DEDICATED TRANSPORTS

UNIT	MODELS PER UNIT	POINTS PER MODEL (Excluding wargear)
Drop Pod	1	63
Impulsor	1	75
Land Speeder Storm	1	55
Razorback	1	70
Repulsor	1	215
Rhino	1	65

FLYERS

UNIT	MODELS PER UNIT	POINTS PER MODEL (Excluding wargear)
Stormhawk Interceptor	1	85
Stormraven Gunship	1	192
Stormtalon Gunship	1	100

RANGED WEAPONS

WEAPON	POINTS PER WEAPON
Absolvor bolt pistol	0
Accelerator autocannon	10
Angelus boltgun	0
Assault bolter	8
Assault cannon	22
Assault plasma incinerator	15
Astartes grenade launcher	6
Astartes shotgun	0
Auto bolt rifle	1
Auto boltstorm gauntlets	12
Bellicatus missile array	17
Bolt carbine	0
Bolt pistol	0
Bolt rifle	0
Bolt sniper rifle	3
Boltgun	0
Boltstorm gauntlet	12
Cerberus launcher	0
Combi-bolter	2
Combi-flamer	8
Combi-grav	13
Combi-melta	15
Combi-plasma	11
Cyclone missile launcher	32
Deathwind launcher	5
Demolisher cannon	0
Flamer	6
Flamestorm cannon	25
Flamestorm gauntlets	14
Frag cannon	20
Frag grenades	0
Fragstorm grenade launcher	4
Grav-cannon and grav-amp	20
Grav-gun	10
Grav-pistol	8
Grenade harness	0
Hand flamer	1
Heavy bolt pistol	0
Heavy bolter	10
Heavy flamer	14
Heavy onslaught gatling cannon	30
Heavy plasma cannon	16
Heavy plasma incinerator	17
Hunter-killer missile	6
Hurricane bolter	10
Icarus ironhail heavy stubber	6
Icarus rocket pod	6
Icarus stormcannon	10
Incendium cannon	15
Inferno pistol	9
Ironhail heavy stubber	6
Kheres pattern assault cannon	22
Krak grenades	0

RANGED WEAPONS

WEAPON	POINTS PER WEAPON
Krakstorm grenade launcher	4
Las-talon	40
Lascannon	25
Macro plasma incinerator	31
Marksman bolt carbine	0
Master-crafted auto bolt rifle	4
Master-crafted boltgun	3
Master-crafted instigator bolt carbine	6
Master-crafted occulus bolt carbine	4
Master-crafted stalker bolt rifle	5
Melta bombs	5
Meltagun	14
Missile launcher	20
Multi-melta	22
Occulus bolt carbine	0
Onslaught gatling cannon	16
Plasma blaster	17
Plasma cannon	16
Plasma cutter	5
Plasma exterminator	17
Plasma gun	11
Plasma incinerator	15
Plasma pistol	5
Predator autocannon	40
Reaper autocannon	10
Reductor pistol	0
Shock grenades	0
Skyhammer missile launcher	20
Skyspear missile launcher	0
Sniper rifle	2
Special issue boltgun	0
Stalker bolt rifle	0
Storm bolter	2
Stormstrike missile launcher	21
Twin assault cannon	44
Twin boltgun	2
Twin heavy bolter	17
Twin heavy plasma cannon	24
Twin Icarus ironhail heavy stubber	10
Twin ironhail autocannon	20
Twin lascannon	40
Twin multi-melta	40
Typhoon missile launcher	32
Volkite charger	3
Whirlwind castellan launcher	15
Whirlwind vengeance launcher	20
Wrist-mounted grenade launcher	0

MELEE WEAPONS

WEAPON	POINTS PER WEAPON
Blood talons	35
Chainfist	11
Chainsword	0
Combat knife	0
Crozius arcanum	0
Dreadnought combat weapon	20
Encarmine axe	9
Encarmine sword	8
Eviscerator	11
Force axe	10
Force stave	8
Force sword	8
Furioso fist (single/pair)	30/40
Furioso force halberd	0
Invictor fist	0
Lightning claws (single/pair)	6/10
Master-crafted power sword	6
Paired combat blades	0
Power axe	5
Power fist	9
Power maul	4
Power sword	4
Redemptor fist	0
Relic blade	9
Servo-arm	0
Thunder hammer (**Characters**)	40
Thunder hammer (other models)	16

OTHER WARGEAR

ITEM	POINTS PER ITEM
Auto launchers	0
Auxiliary grenade launcher	1
Camo cloak	3
Combat shield	1
Death mask	2
Grapnel launcher	2
Grav-chute	2
Haywire mine	10
Magna-grapple	5
Orbital comms array	18
Shield dome	18
Smoke grenades	0
Storm shield (**Characters**)	10
Storm shield (other models)	2
Teleport homer	0

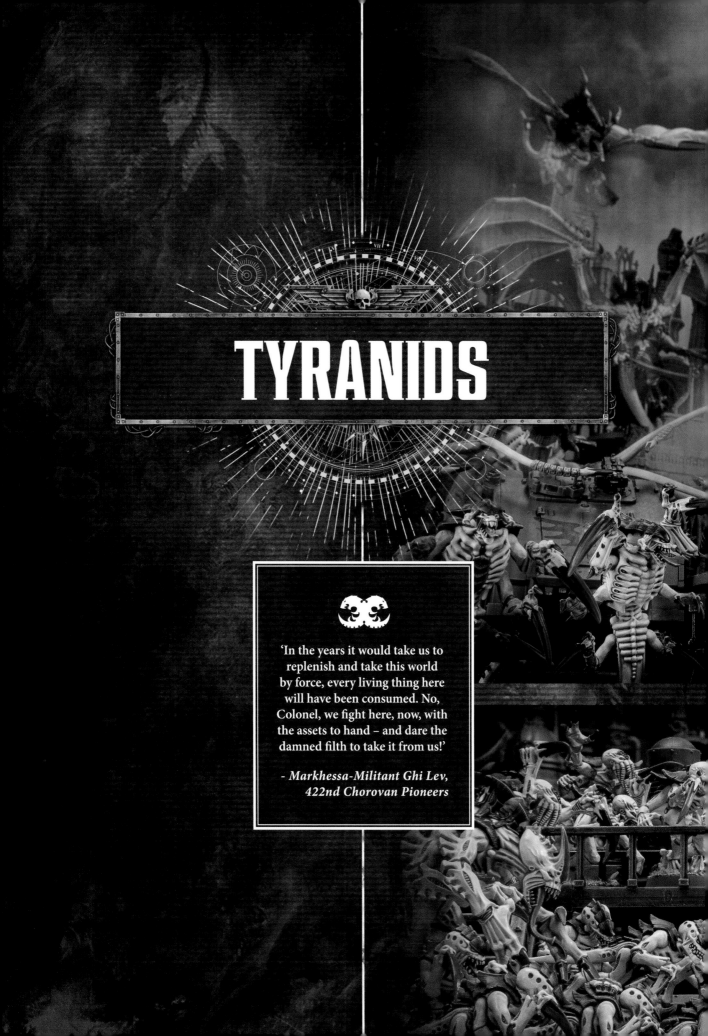

TYRANIDS

'In the years it would take us to replenish and take this world by force, every living thing here will have been consumed. No, Colonel, we fight here, now, with the assets to hand – and dare the damned filth to take it from us!'

- Markhessa-Militant Ghi Lev, 422nd Chorovan Pioneers

INEXORABLE ADAPTATION

This section contains new and updated rules for *Codex: Tyranids*, including Relics, Stratagems, a Tyranids name generator, Hive Fleet-specific psychic powers, and rules for creating custom Hive Fleet Adaptations for your Tyranids Detachments.

In the rules described in this section we often refer to 'Tyranids units'. This is shorthand for any **TYRANIDS** unit that also has the **<HIVE FLEET>** keyword. A Tyranids Detachment is therefore one that only includes units with both the **TYRANIDS** and **<HIVE FLEET>** keyword.

Note that although Genestealer Cults are devoted to the Hive Mind and will willingly fight alongside their xenos masters, they deviate significantly in terms of organisation and tactics, not to mention physiology! **GENESTEALER CULTS** units therefore cannot make use of any of the rules listed in this section (this includes the Detachment abilities, Stratagems, Relics and psychic powers in this section), and instead have their own rules.

Bio-Artefacts

On the page opposite you will find a selection of new Bio-artefacts of the Tyranids detailing some of the more grotesque and horrifying aberations that this alien race has brought to bear against its foes. These can be taken instead of one of those detailed in *Codex: Tyranids*.

Stratagems

Here you will find a number of new Stratagems usable by Tyranids Detachments. These can be used in addition to those found in *Codex: Tyranids*, and bring a new range of tactical options and unique behaviour to the creatures of the Hive Mind.

Adaptive Physiology

The Hive Mind is capable of adapting and changing even the most basic biological facets of its creations in order to better combat and overcome its enemies. This section contains rules for altering a unit in your Tyranids army with a unique adaptative physiology, tailor-made to destroy your adversary's forces.

Hive Fleet Adaptations

On pages 74-75 you will find rules for creating your own Hive Fleet Adaptations. These comprise a selection of abilities that can be combined to create a hive fleet of your own devising, or be used to represent one of the Hive Fleets in our publications that is not currently represented by a Hive Fleet Adaptation in *Codex: Tyranids*.

Hive Fleet Psychic Powers

In this section you will find new hive fleet-specific psychic powers, allowing the unique psychic footprint of these fleets to manifest themselves on the battlefield in new and dangerous ways.

Name Generator

The final section contains a name generator for your Tyranid organisms, allowing you to further personalise units from your army.

BIO-ARTEFACTS OF THE TYRANIDS

Spawned by the hive fleets to further the Hive Mind's inscrutable will, each of these rare and powerful symbiotic organisms has gestated spontaneously in some unfathomable biological mechanism –and in many guises – over the Tyranid race's immeasurable existence.

If your army is led by a Tyranids Warlord, you can give one of the following Bio-artefacts to a Tyranids **Character** model from your army instead of giving them a Bio-artefact from *Codex: Tyranids*. Named characters cannot be given any of the following Bio-Artefacts.

Note that some Bio-artefacts are items of wargear that replace one of the model's existing items of wargear. Where this is the case, you must, if you are using points values, still pay the cost of the wargear being replaced. Write down any Bio-Artefacts your models have on your army roster.

RESONANCE BARB

Within the crowning carapace of this creature are pulsing bundles of nerves, their tendrils driven irreversibly into the beast's cortex. The Resonance Barb throbs at sympathetic frequencies with the Hive Mind, transmitting a portion of its cosmic might into the creature's flesh-form.

Psyker model only. A model with this Relic can attempt to manifest one additional psychic power in your Psychic phase and attempt to deny one additional psychic power in your opponent's Psychic phase. In addition, when a Psychic test is taken for a model with this Relic, add 1 to the total.

XENOGENIC ACID

This oily black subtance continually seeps from the swollen cysts of its carrier. Splashes of the liquid have been seen to flow against gravity towards horrified eyes or compromised armour plates, giving rise to speculation that the acid itself is sentient. Within moments, the horrifying effluence finds its way inside its victims, breaking down the prey's genetic structure and molecular cohesion until all that is left is a bubbling pile of black bio-matter.

Model with toxin sacs only. This Relic replaces toxin sacs. When resolving a melee attack made by a model with this Relic, an unmodified wound roll of 5+ inflicts 1 mortal wound on the target in addition to any other damage.

THE VENOMTHORN PARASITE

These engorged bio-ammunition tubes are only the outer form of an ancient symbiotic intelligence that spreads its nerve endings like a fungus throughout both creature and weapon, neurally linking the three together. When it senses prey, the Venomthorn Parasite dominates its two hosts, pushing the weapon symbiote to its limit with pulses of hormonal stimuli until the target is eviscerated.

Model equipped with a stranglethorn cannon and/or heavy venom cannon only. When this model shoots with a stranglethorn cannon or heavy venom cannon, do not roll any dice when determining the Type characteristic of that weapon; instead it has the maximum value (e.g. a Heavy D6 weapon makes 6 attacks).

PATHOGENESIS

An organism like no other, Pathogenesis is perhaps a throwback to the Tyranids' genetic origins, or a shadow of things to come. Though its motes of psychic awareness are diffused throughout its carrier like a virus, it acts with a singular will. Subverting the body and symbiotes of its host, Pathogenesis causes rapid mutation: cartilaginous tubes and containment spines are lengthened; intercostal muscles are engorged; bio-ammunition are sheathed in a toxic dermis. With its host's reach and lethality extended, fragments of Pathogenesis can reach out to the bodies of many more prey, by infesting the bio-ammunition or riding through the bio-electric charge. Whether it aims only to spread itself or is actively seeking something in the bodies of its fallen foes, perhaps only time will tell.

Add 8" to the Range characteristic of ranged weapons a model with this Relic is equipped with. In addition, when a model with this Relic fires Overwatch or is chosen to shoot with, you can re-roll a single hit roll and you can re-roll a single wound roll.

ARACHNACYTE GLAND

The Arachnacyte Gland clutches the spine of its host bioform, its multi-limbed tendrils becoming wedded to the creature's own flesh. Through these, the bio-artefact floods its host's nervous systems and organs and lashes it with psychic stimuli, driving the beast on ever faster.

Model with adrenal glands only. This Relic replaces adrenal glands. When a charge roll is made for a model with this Relic, roll one additional D6 and discard one of the dice. In addition, when an Advance roll is made for a model with this Relic, add 1 to the result.

STRATAGEMS

If your army is Battle-forged and includes any Tyranids Detachments (excluding Auxiliary Support Detachments), you have access to the Stratagems shown here, and can spend Command Points to activate them. These reflect the unique strategies used by the forces of the Hive Mind on the battlefield.

GRASPING TENDRILS
Tyranids Stratagem
None escape the deadly reach of these toxic appendages.

1CP

Use this Stratagem in your opponent's Movement phase, when an enemy unit that does not have a minimum Move characteristic and is within 1" of any **TOXICRENE** units from your army is chosen to Fall Back. Roll one D6, adding 1 to the result if that unit is an **INFANTRY** unit; on a 3+ that enemy unit cannot Fall Back this turn.

SYMBIOTIC DEVASTATION
Tyranids Stratagem
In thrall to its symbiote, the Exocrine obeys its every will.

1CP

Use this Stratagem at the start of your Shooting phase. Select one **EXOCRINE** unit from your army; until the end of that phase, that unit is treated as not having moved in your Movement phase.

SURPRISE AMBUSH
Tyranids Stratagem
Lictors can approach within feet of their prey unnoticed.

1CP

Use this Stratagem in your Charge phase. Select one **LICTOR** unit from your army that is entirely on or within a terrain feature, or was set up on the battlefield this turn using the Hidden Hunter ability. Until the end of the turn, enemy units cannot fire Overwatch at that unit. In addition, when a charge roll is made for that unit, add 1 to the result.

FERAL INSTINCTS
Tyranids Stratagem
Talons are unconsciously directed at throats and eyes.

1CP

Use this Stratagem in the Fight phase. Select one **HORMAGAUNTS** unit from your army. Until the end of that phase, improve the Armour Penetration characteristic of melee weapons models in that unit are equipped with by 1 (e.g. AP 0 becomes AP -1).

FEEDING THE HUNGER
Tyranids Stratagem
The Haruspex's instinctive need to consume is insatiable.

1CP

Use this Stratagem in the Fight phase, when a **HARUSPEX** unit from your army is chosen to fight wtih. Until the end of that phase, when resolving an attack made by that model, you can re-roll the hit roll.

UNEXPECTED INCURSION
Tyranids Stratagem
Mawlocs are capable of bursts of subterranean speed, catching more of their surface prey unawares.

1CP

Use this Stratagem in your Movement phase, when a **MAWLOC** model from your army is set up on the battlefield using the Terror from the Deep ability. When determining the number of mortal wounds an enemy unit suffers from that model's Terror from the Deep ability that phase, add 2 to the roll.

BURIED THREATS
Tyranids Stratagem
Burrowing feeder organisms can surge just beneath the surface, their advance shrouded in sprays of earth.

1CP

Use this Stratagem in your Movement phase, when a **RIPPERS** unit from your army is set up on the battlefield using the Burrowers ability. For as long as that unit remains stationary, when resolving an attack made with a ranged weapon against that unit, subtract 1 from the hit roll.

SAVAGE DISTRACTION
Tyranids Stratagem
With their comrades' gore dripping from nearby talons, even disciplined warriors struggle to avert their guns.

1CP

Use this Stratagem in the Fight phase, when an enemy unit is destroyed as a result of an attack made by a model in a **<HIVE FLEET>** unit from your army. In your opponent's next Shooting phase, when resolving an attack made with a ranged weapon by an enemy model within 6" of that **<HIVE FLEET>** unit against another unit from your army, subtract 1 from the hit roll.

HIVE INSTINCT

1CP

Tyranids Stratagem

With a psychic summons, the swarm is gathered.

Use this Stratagem in your Charge phase. Select one enemy unit that is within 1" of any <**Hive Fleet**> **Synapse** units from your army. Until the end of that phase, when a charge roll is made for a charge made by a friendly <**Hive Fleet**> unit that targets that enemy unit, roll one additional D6 and discard one of the dice. The first model you move as part of that charge must end its charge move within 1" of that enemy unit, otherwise the charge fails and no models in the charging unit move this phase.

UNYIELDING CHITIN

1CP

Tyranids Stratagem

At a synaptic stimulus, carapaces thicken to become as dense as stone.

Use this Stratagem in your Charge phase or your opponent's Shooting phase, when a **Tyranid Prime** or **Tyranid Warriors** unit from your army is chosen as the target for an attack made with a ranged weapon. Until the end of that phase, when resolving an attack made with a ranged weapon against that unit, reduce the Damage characteristic of that weapon by 1, to a minimum of 1, for that attack.

ENCEPHALIC DIFFUSION

2CP

Tyranids Stratagem

Glistening brain-arrays pulse with diffusive energies.

Use this Stratagem at the start of the turn. Select one **Maleceptor** model from your army. Until the end of that turn, when resolving an attack made with a ranged weapon against a friendly unit within 6" of that model, subtract 1 from that weapon's Strength characteristic, to a minimum of 1, for that attack.

AGGRESSIVE ADAPTATION

1CP

Tyranids Stratagem

Biomorphic resin sharpens at the touch of enemy blood.

Use this Stratagem in the Fight phase, when an enemy unit is destroyed as a result of an attack made by a <**Hive Fleet**> model from your army. Until the end of the battle, improve the Armour Penetration characteristic of melee weapons that models in that model's unit are equipped with by 1 (e.g. AP 0 becomes AP -1). Each unit can only be affected by this Stratagem once per battle.

SYNAPTIC CHANNELLING

1CP

Tyranids Stratagem

Individuality is a disadvantage that Tyranids surpass.

Use this Stratagem in your Psychic phase. Select one <**Hive Fleet**> **Psyker** unit from your army. Until the end of that phase, that unit knows all of the psychic powers known by friendly <**Hive Fleet**> **Psyker** units that are on the battlefield.

SKYSWARM FUSILLADE

1CP

Tyranids Stratagem

The instinctive and fluid agility of skyswarm bioforms allow acidic shots to be fired at extreme close-quarters.

Use this Stratagem in your Shooting phase. Select one **Gargoyles** unit from your army. Until the end of the phase, fleshborers that models in that unit are equipped with have a Type characteristic of Pistol 1.

PSYCHIC FISSURE

2CP

Tyranids Stratagem

The Shadow in the Warp poses many dangers to those who would draw upon the immaterium's energies.

Use this Stratagem at the start of your opponent's Psychic phase. Until the end of that phase, when a Psychic test is taken for an enemy unit within 12" of any <**Hive Fleet**> **Synapse** units from your army and the test is failed, that enemy unit suffers D3 mortal wounds.

HUNTER'S DRIVE

1CP

Tyranids Stratagem

Saturating its kills with motes of synaptic energy, the leader-beast drives its minions towards any survivors.

Use this Stratagem in your Charge phase. Select one <**Hive Fleet**> unit from your army. Until the end of the phase, when that unit declares a charge that targets any enemy units that had one or more models destroyed as a result of attacks made with ranged weapons made by friendly <**Hive Fleet**> **Synapse** models this turn, roll one additional D6 and discard one of the dice when making the charge roll. The first model you move as part of that charge must end its charge move within 1" of at least one of those units, otherwise the charge fails and no models in the charging unit move this phase.

HIVE FLEET ADAPTATIONS

The Tyranid race is a single, gestalt super-organism, preying on the entire galaxy. Yet like the variable nature of its bio-horrors, each hive fleet is an expression of the Tyranids' adaptability. The huge number of hive fleets allows the Tyranids to deploy an unending array of deadly morphic traits.

Codex: Tyranids describes how the <Hive Fleet> keyword can be substituted with the name of your chosen Hive Fleet, as well as describing the abilities that units in Tyranids Detachments gain. One of these abilities is Hive Fleet Adaptations. If your chosen Hive Fleet does not have an associated Hive Fleet Adaptation in *Codex: Tyranids*, you can create its Hive Fleet Adaptation by selecting two different rules from the following list:

Adaptive Exoskeleton

The gaunt-derived creatures produced by some hive fleets secrete a waxy, resinous material that hardens into a slick layer of protection, deflecting or absorbing hits.

Termagant, Hormagaunt and Gargoyle models with this adaptation have a 6+ invulnerable save.

Bestial Nature

The monstrous organisms of this hive fleet embody a savage ferocity. When wounded near unto death, they lash out in animalistic fury, making taking them down a suicidal prospect.

Add 2 to the Attacks characteristic of a model with this adaptation that has a damage table whilst using the bottom row of that model's damage table.

Bio-metallic Cysts

Incubated within the bladed limbs of this hive fleet's weapon-beasts are colonies of cysts whose bio-metallic edges can slice through armour.

Improve the Armour Penetration characteristic of Scything Talons that models with this adaptation are equipped with by 1 (e.g. AP 0 becomes AP -1).

Biosphere Consumption

Parasitising upon the prey world itself, this hive fleet's monstrosities delve osmotic tendrils into its biomass. Embedding themselves like a tumour and fuelling their metabolic resilience, they are nigh impossible to remove.

When a Monster model with this adaptation would lose a wound, if that model's unit did not move during your last Movement phase or it is the first battle round, and there are no enemy units within 1" of that model's unit, roll one D6; on a 6 that wound is not lost.

Cranial Channelling

The craniums of this hive fleet's psyker-beasts contain a clutch of symbiotic larvae whose entire life-cycle revolves around the channelling of the Hive Mind. With an instinctive impulse, the carrier will absorb one of these creatures into their swollen brain matter, thus becoming a more efficient and fluid extension of the hive fleet's will.

Once per turn, when a Psychic test is taken for a model with this adaptation, you can re-roll the result.

Feeding Frenzy

With dormant glands that suddenly burst into life, and reinforced, adaptive cartilage powering headlong leaps, the swarms of this hive fleet feed their urge to close with their prey as quickly as possible.

When a pile-in move is made for a unit with this adaptation, models in that unit can move up to 6" instead of 3".

Horror from Beyond

Whether due to some sickening aura of the Hive Mind or simply their terrifying size and predatory hunger, this hive fleet's larger organisms are so monstrous that few are the heroic or insane who can stand before them.

Subtract 1 from the Leadership characteristic of models in enemy units whilst their unit is within 3" of any Monster units from your army with this adaptation.

Hypermetabolic Acceleration

This hive fleet bio-engineers its horrors with multiple stimm-releasing glands. Surges of extragalactic chemicals drive them to frenzied rushes across the prey worlds.

When a unit with this adaptation Advances, you can re-roll the Advance roll.

Membranous Mobility

This hive fleet's skyswarm bioforms evince an unusually complex web of membranous tissue, allowing them to weave and jink with such astounding flexibility that carefully aimed blows can easily pass through thin air.

When resolving an attack made with a melee weapon against a model with this adaptation that can Fly, subtract 1 from the hit roll.

Metamorphic Regrowth

Within the flesh of its limitless broods, this hive fleet has adapted strange conglomerate organs and pathogen-hunting spores that can rapidly reknit any damage.

A model with this adaptation regains up to 1 lost wound at the start of your turn.

Morphic Sinews

Stabilised with fibrous cords of sinew and internal wells of viscous fluid, this hive fleet's largest weapon symbiotes instinctively adjust to their host beast's hulking advances.

MONSTER models with this adaptation do not suffer the penalty for moving and firing Heavy weapons, nor for Advancing and firing Assault weapons.

Pack Hunters

Submerging their prey in waves of talons and fangs, this hive fleet's creatures use their weight of numbers to punch and tear their way through once-stout defences.

When resolving an attack made with a melee weapon by a model with this adaptation against a unit that contains fewer models than that model's unit, improve the Armour Penetration characteristic of that weapon by 1 for that attack (e.g. AP 0 become AP -1).

Prey-sight

Some hive fleets' horrifying colossi close with the enemy while straining their multiple alien senses, the prey's every movement and position noted. When it comes, the strike is inescapable.

If a MONSTER unit with this adaptation makes a charge move, is charged or performs a Heroic Intervention, then until the end of the turn, when resolving an attack made with a melee weapon by a model in that unit, add 1 to the hit roll.

Senses of the Outer Dark

Developed beyond the galaxy, this hive fleet's organisms' preternatural senses are triggered by surges of aggression as they close with the enemy. The prey's fearful defensive fire is dodged with blinding speed.

When a model with this adaptation would lose a wound as a result of an Overwatch attack, roll one D6; on a 4+ that wound is not lost.

Shrewd Predators

This hive fleet's synaptic coordination is so overwhelming that it compels its organisms to override their baser instincts, unnervingly moving in unexpected directions – all the while closing the snare on their prey.

When a model with this adaptation makes a consolidation move, if there are no enemy models within 3", that model does not have to end the move closer to the nearest enemy model.

Sporemist Spines

Ejected with a muscular spasm from between carapace plates, these clouds of microscopic crystalline spines cause pain and disorientation, allowing this hive fleet's broods to slip away at speed – and on to meatier prey.

A unit with this adaptation can Advance in a turn in which it Falls Back.

Synaptic Augmentation

This hive fleet has refined its conduits to the lesser organisms, allowing for subtle control and augmentation of their instincts. So directed, they are far more deadly.

When a <HIVE FLEET> unit with this adaptation that is within 6" of a friendly <HIVE FLEET> PSYKER or <HIVE FLEET> SYNAPSE unit fires Overwatch or is chosen to shoot or fight with, you can re-roll a single hit roll.

ADAPTIVE PHYSIOLOGY

The Hive Mind is a vast, galaxy-spanning intelligence, unhampered by the petty boundaries of mortality that benights the galaxy's other races. If a brood of weapon-beasts or a near-mindless monstrosity has proved advantageous, its traits and adaptations – once reabsorbed by the hive fleets – will be born anew.

If a Tyranids **CHARACTER** is your Warlord, rather than determining a Warlord Trait for that model, you can instead select an Adaptive Physiology for one Tyranids unit from your army. To do so, before the battle begins select one Tyranids **INFANTRY** unit or one Tyranids **MONSTER** model from your army, and select an Adaptive Physiology from the corresponding list below. That Adaptive Physiology applies to the selected model or unit until the end of the battle. Write down any Adaptive Physiologies your models have on your army roster.

If you have a Tyranids **CHARACTER** in your army, you also have access to the Progeny of the Hive Stratagem below:

> **1CP**
>
> ## PROGENY OF THE HIVE
> *Tyranids Stratagem*
> *Nothing can hold back the terrifying speed at which the hive fleets adapt their diverse organisms.*
>
> Use this Stratagem before the battle. Select one Tyranids **INFANTRY** unit or one Tyranids **MONSTER** model from your army that does not have an Adaptive Physiology, and then select one Adaptive Physiology to apply to that unit or model until the end of the battle. You can only use this Stratagem once per battle.

INFANTRY ADAPTIVE PHYSIOLOGIES

If you selected an **INFANTRY** unit, you can select from the following list of Adaptive Physiologies.

Enhanced Resistance
The subcutaneous fibroid membranes of these bioforms are capable of absorbing even armour-piercing shots and blows.

When resolving an attack made against this unit with a weapon that has an Armour Penetration characteristic of -1 or -2, that weapon has an Armour Penetration characteristic of 0 for that attack.

Adrenal Webs
With battlefield knowledge gained from devouring the fleeter races of the galaxy, this brood's glandular stimuli drives them forwards at an unprecedented speed, allowing none to escape.

When this unit consolidates, it can move up to 2D6" instead of 3".

Abhorrent Pheremones
The brood releases a complex chemical signature in the press of fighting that provokes fear responses in their prey. Confused and panicking, the enemy are easily torn down.

Subtract 2 from the Leadership characteristic of models in enemy units whilst their unit is within 1" of this unit.

Dynamic Camouflage
Chromatospores in this brood's skin and carapace adapt at a frightening pace, seamlessly blending their alien forms into their surroundings.

When resolving an attack made with a ranged weapon against a model from this unit that is receiving the benefit of cover, add 2 to the saving throw instead of 1.

Unnatural Reactions
This brood uses unique alien senses and its connection to the Hive Mind to react instantly to prey attacking other Tyranids nearby.

This unit can perform Heroic Interventions as if it were a **CHARACTER**. In addition, this unit can perform a Heroic Intervention if there are any enemy units within 6" of them instead of 3", and when doing so can move up to 6" instead of 3".

MONSTER ADAPTIVE PHYSIOLOGIES

If you selected a **MONSTER** model, you can select from the following list of Adaptive Physiologies.

Dermic Symbiosis
This bio-horror's carapace is actually a symbiotic organism, capable of psychically repelling the fiercest attacks of the prey and boosting the metabolism of its host creature.

This model has a 5+ invulnerable save. In addition, if this model has a damage table it is considered to have double the number of wounds remaining for the purposes of determining what row to use on that damage table.

Voracious Ammunition

Either host to nests of ever-hungry bio-ammunition or unique organs generating a constant stream of bio-chemical substances, this xenos brute's far-reaching touch continues to sear and consume long after it has moved on to other prey.

At the end of your Shooting phase, select one enemy unit that had one or more models destroyed this phase as a result of an attack made by this model. That unit suffers D3 mortal wounds.

Accelerated Digestion

The ravenous hunger of this monstrous creature is complemented by a dizzying array of consumption sacs and ferociously powerful digestive acids, fuelling its alien vitality with every screaming morsel of prey.

In the Fight phase, when an enemy model is destroyed as a result of an attack made by this model, this model regains up to 1 lost wound. No more than 3 lost wounds can be regained as a result of this rule in any one turn.

Synaptic Enhancement

Adaptations to this organism's cerebral architecture have enhanced its connection to the Hive Mind. Through this towering and deadly creature, the horrific control and influence of the Tyranid race is spread ever further.

This model gains the Shadow in the Warp and Synapse abilities (see *Codex: Tyranids*), and gains the SYNAPSE keyword.

Murderous Size

Whether enormous osseous blades, writhing lashes or oversized fangs, this colossus' means of rending apart its prey have grown far beyond those of its kind. Fuelled by the bearer's instinctive ability to slay, each hideous blow and crushing bite delivered by these bio-weapons hasten the prey world's demise.

Before the battle, select one melee weapon that this model is equipped with. Until the end of the battle, add 1 to the Strength and Damage characteristics of that weapon, and improve the Armour Penetration characteristic of that weapon by 1 (e.g. AP 0 becomes AP -1).

HIVE FLEET PSYCHIC POWERS

Just as individual broods display varying genetic adaptations and swarms adopt different strategies, so do the hive fleets' psyker-beasts manifest fragments of the Hive Mind's gestalt will in diverse, predatory ways.

All <Hive Fleet> Psyker models can know the psychic power of their respective Hive Fleet. Instead of generating a psychic power from the Hive Mind discipline (see *Codex: Tyranids*), a <Hive Fleet> Psyker can instead know the appropriate Hive Fleet psychic power from the list below.

BEHEMOTH: UNSTOPPABLE HUNGER

The Hive Mind siphons into its organisms a tiny portion of Behemoth's insatiable and aeons-long hunger. Filled with an aching void, claws and talons rend ever more desperately in their need to feed.

Unstoppable Hunger has a warp charge value of 7. If manifested, select one friendly **Behemoth** unit within 9" of this psyker. Until the end of the turn, when resolving an attack made with a melee weapon by a model in that unit, add 1 to the wound roll.

KRAKEN: SYNAPTIC LURE

Drawing upon Kraken's strategic cunning, the Hive Mind projects a psychic marker upon an identified threat. Unknowingly radiating an irresistible lure to every nearby brood, the enemy is doomed.

Synaptic Lure has a warp charge value of 5. If manifested, select one enemy unit. Until the end of the turn, when a charge roll is made for a charge made by a friendly **Kraken** unit that targets that enemy unit, you can re-roll the result.

LEVIATHAN: HIVE NEXUS

The Hive Mind funnels Leviathan's sophisticated synaptic network through its conduits, enforcing its gestalt will among the hive fleet's lesser organisms.

Hive Nexus has a warp charge value of 6. If manifested, until the start of your next Psychic phase, the range of the Synapse ability for friendly **Leviathan** units is 18", instead of 12".

GORGON: POISONOUS INFLUENCE

The synapse creature radiates a pulsed imperative which triggers the semi-sentient spores of Gorgon's bio-horrors, guiding the secretion of venom laced with a seeping psychic miasma.

Poisonous Influence has a warp charge value of 6. If manifested, until the start of your next Psychic phase, improve the Armour Penetration characteristic of melee weapons that friendly models within 9" of this psyker are equipped with by 1 (e.g. AP 0 becomes AP -1).

JORMUNGANDR: LURKING MAWS

The Hive Mind extends a psychic summons, and calls upon Jormungandr's embedded and waiting broods. Mindlessly converging via synaptic imperative, their sudden and frenzied attacks spell the foe's end.

Lurking Maws has a warp charge value of 6. If manifested, select one enemy unit that is visible to this psyker. Until the end of the turn, when resolving an attack against that unit made by a model in a friendly **Jormungandr** unit that was set up on the battlefield this turn, you can re-roll the hit roll. This psychic power cannot be manifested in the first battle round.

HYDRA: DEATH SHRIEK

Amplifying the psychic death cry of Hydra's progeny to horrifying levels, the Hive Mind causes excruciating physical and psychic trauma in those who resist its predations.

Death Shriek has a warp charge value of 5. If manifested, until the start of your next Psychic phase, when a friendly **Hydra** model within 6" of this psyker and within 6" of any enemy units is destroyed, roll one D6; on a 6, the closest enemy unit to that **Hydra** model suffers 1 mortal wound.

KRONOS: SYMBIOSTORM

The Hive Mind delves into the neural mesh between Kronos' organisms and their symbiotes. Guided by its majestic will, a deluge of shrieking bio-matter reaches out unerringly towards the Tyranids' prey.

Symbiostorm has a warp charge value of 6. If manifested, select one friendly **Kronos** unit within 12" of this psyker. Until the end of the turn, when resolving an attack made with a ranged weapon by a model in that unit, a hit roll of 6+ scores 1 additional hit.

NAME GENERATOR

The Tyranids do not have names, the Hive Mind's progeny as insignificant to each other as human blood cells. Their enemies, however, often grant horrific epithets to monstrous and scuttling forms seen to haunt the battlefields of the 41st Millennium. Whispers along trenchlines and dire warnings committed to vox tell of certain broods seen time and again. If you wish to randomly generate a name for one of your Tyranid broods, you can roll a D66 and consult the table below. To roll a D66, simply roll two D6, one after the other – the first represents tens, and the second represents digits, giving you a result between 11 and 66.

D66	FIRST ELEMENT	D66	SECOND ELEMENT
11	The Omega	11	Infestation
12	The Creeping	12	Talon
13	The Blooded	13	Fang
14	The Venomous	14	Claw
15	The Shifting	15	Tendril
16	The Benighted	16	Coil
21	The Caustic	21	Eye
22	The Serpent's	22	Brood
23	The Alpha	23	Shadow
24	The Rising	24	Dread
25	The Consuming	25	Swarm
26	The Looming	26	Barb
31	The Grasping	31	Jaws
32	The Ravening	32	Assassins
33	The Kolorian	33	Slayers
34	The Icharian	34	Executioners
35	The Writhing	35	Ghosts
36	The Inescapable	36	Echo
41	The Dark	41	Terrors
42	Hell's	42	Horrors
43	The Nightmare	43	Lurkers
44	The Rending	44	Heralds
45	The Ominous	45	Sting
46	The Outer	46	Bite
51	The Ancient	51	Doom
52	The Slithering	52	Butchers
53	The Bladed	53	Devils
54	The Monstrous	54	Wraiths
55	The Elder	55	Menace
56	The Nameless	56	Shroud
61	The Hunter's	61	Annihilators
62	The Formless	62	Scream
63	The Sudden	63	Pall
64	The Void	64	Devourers
65	The Prowling	65	Stalkers
66	The Hungry	66	Maw

'How much horror can the Emperor's subjects endure? How much death? Day by day we drive these xenos back. Day by day they overwhelm and devour us in their turn. Always there comes another wave, another tendril. Never has the Emperor's light shone as brightly amidst the shadows of the Red Scar, yet perhaps it is this that draws the aliens to us from the outer dark? Perhaps. It begins in blood, and in blood it ends… I know what must be done…'

- Mephiston, the Lord of Death